COMMUNICATING WITH

LEADER GUIDE

by Simon and Karen Fox

Santa Barbara, CA

Communicating with Compassion
Leader Guide
By Simon and Karen Fox

Adventures in Caring Foundation
P.O. Box 3859
Santa Barbara, CA 93130
(805) 687-5803
(800) 833-5678
(805) 563-7678 (fax)

ISBN 0-9655803-0-X

Thank You

The *Communicating with Compassion* video and leader guide was made possible by Pierre P. Claeyssens and a grant from the Wood-Claeyssens Foundation, in loving memory of Ailene B. Claeyssens.

Book and Cover Design: Kathy Fritz and Brenna Pierce
    of Fritz Creative
Editor: Pam Hamlin
Discussion Design: J.W. Ballard of Winning Teams
Consultants: Jill Morris, Pat Wheatley, Richard Medway
Photography: Simon Fox
Desktop Publishing Equipment: Santa Barbara Foundation
Special Support: Santa Barbara Cottage Hospital
Special Support: Rotary Club of Santa Barbara, Downtown

Special thanks to the following people for their friendship, encouragement and inspiration:
    Anthony Allina, M.D.
    Anna Bissell, R.N.
    Pierre Claeyssens
    Eliot Cowan
    Alice Cox
    John Davies
    Johnny and Claudine Fincioen
    Michael Fisher, M.D.
    Stephen Hosea, M.D.
    Sir George King, D.D.
    Margaret Norvell
    Bruce O'Neal
    The Poor Clare Sisters
    John Rathbone, D.D.S.
    Dean Smith
    Adventures in Caring Foundation board of directors,
        advisors, volunteers and supporters

COMMUNICATING WITH
Compassion

Welcome

Karen S. Fox

Producing *Communicating with Compassion* has been a team effort. Physicians, nurses, administrators, patients, family members and hundreds of volunteers have contributed to its design.

The skills and insights we present in the video are the result of over thirteen years experience running volunteer programs in hospitals and nursing homes. Since 1984 our volunteers have made more than 250,000 visits to people who are seriously ill, lonely, or dying. All of these individual interactions have helped us build a substantial body of knowledge about the kind of communication that is, and is not, appreciated, when giving assistance to someone in need.

From this body of knowledge we have distilled four key elements that make it easier for people to accept and appreciate assistance. These Four Elements are vividly illustrated in the video by real life situations. They are the vital ingredients that make interactions meaningful, uplifting and satisfying to all involved. They are also four basic human needs:

1. Attention
2. Acknowledgment
3. Affection
4. Acceptance

Communicating with Compassion is the art of interacting with people who are suffering – in ways that empower, encourage, bring hope and lift the spirit. Our vision is for those who give of themselves, whether they are volunteers, staff, or family members, to know how to communicate compassionately with the people they help; so that the support they give in a time of need, is that much more effective.

What you are about to see is a forty-minute video that is both instructional and inspirational. With the group leader guide and handouts you can make it into a ninety-minute presentation, or a three-hour workshop.

The program is designed for use by leaders of staff and volunteers, in hospitals, long-term care centers, retirement centers, healthcare agencies, high schools, colleges, churches, temples, youth groups and other community service organizations.

Communicating with Compassion provides a ready-made training session – a session that will inspire your audience, and give them the tools to improve their skills.

Thank you for being a part of the team that makes this learning experience possible. We couldn't make it available without you.

I hope that *Communicating with Compassion* will help you in your efforts to make a difference.

With love,

Karen S. Fox

Karen S. Fox
Founder/Director
Adventures in Caring Foundation

P.S. Every day I continue learning about life, by serving others. I continue learning how to love more fully, by applying the Four Elements described in the video.

I hope that all those with whom you share this video, will walk away from the experience with a newfound enthusiasm; and with eyes to see the true beauty and satisfaction of putting compassion into action.

TABLE OF CONTENTS

INTRODUCTION

1

INTRODUCTION

1

A NEW APPROACH

Communicating with Compassion is a new approach to learning communication skills. It shows how volunteers, family members and staff deal with real life situations.

All of the interactions in the video, with the exception of the "bloopers" scenes[1], were filmed naturally. The people had never met before you see them on the screen. Some scenes are from a minute or two into their first meeting, but not longer. No visits were rehearsed or planned in any way. No prior introductions were made. What you see is what happened, between real volunteers and real patients, on a normal day in a real hospital.

The advantage of this approach is that you won't get comments from your audience such as "no-one talks like that," or "get real, that's not how people act." The other advantage is that these scenes give people a realistic preparation for assisting others, because it shows what it looks, sounds and feels like when you are helping someone in distress.

You may, however, get comments such as, "Who are these people? They make it look so easy." The answer is, they are all volunteers with Adventures in Caring, trained by Karen Fox in the same method shown in this video. Each of them have at least two years experience in visiting people who are seriously ill.

WHO CAN USE THIS VIDEO?

This video is filmed on location in hospitals, nursing homes, retirement centers and in the home. However, these communication skills apply to any situation where someone is facing a tough challenge and needs to know that someone cares. Such situations include:

1 The only exceptions are the "blooper" scenes where we show the mistakes people make. Even these scenes are unscripted and not performed by actors, but by volunteers who have experienced similar situations.

- a serious illness or injury
- death and dying
- isolation, abandonment or loneliness (such as people shut-in at home)
- severe poverty or homelessness
- abuse, violence or trauma
- a family or relationship breaking apart
- losing someone or something important: a loved one, a job, an ability
- intense stress, grief and distress in many forms

N O T E : You will need to point out to your group that, although the scenes may not portray the exact situations they deal with, the skills demonstrated are still applicable in the circumstances listed above. This could be a valuable teaching point: Ask your group how they could apply these skills to their particular job.

YOUR OPPORTUNITY

As a group leader you have an opportunity to make a difference in the lives of many people, not only those in your class, but everyone they help, and even their families and friends. You have an opportunity to cultivate greater compassion in your community, and we sincerely hope that the *Communicating with Compassion* videotape and written materials will help you to do just this.

Communicating with Compassion presents skills that increase the capacity to assist others. It is an opportunity to make volunteer or professional work more meaningful, more satisfying, more effective and more appreciated.

To get the most benefit from this video, the audience needs your leadership. Without a meaningful discussion of the video, a class is limited in the depth of understanding they can gain – and this is where your leadership comes in.

Using the steps outlined in this Leader Guide, you can help the audience achieve greater insight – not by telling them what to do – but by guiding an exchange of ideas and perspectives. The step-by-step details of how to do this are in chapters 2 and 3 of this Leader Guide.

"There is hunger for ordinary bread, and there is hunger for love, for kindness, for thoughtfulness; and this is the great poverty that makes people suffer so much."

– MOTHER TERESA OF CALCUTTA

For those who, like most of us, are a little nervous about leading a group, we have simplified the task. All you have to do is ask a series of questions which we have already written for you.

For example, you will ask a few brief questions to get the group involved and ready to learn, before showing the video. Afterwards, you will ask a series of questions that guide a thirty-minute discussion about the video. This completes the basic ninety-minute learning session (see chapter 2.)

You can build on this basic method, adapt it to your needs, and make it more complex, but the essence is very simple.

If the class formats described in chapters 2 and 3 don't meet your needs, you can customize the learning session using: the handouts on the Four Elements in the back of this Leader Guide; the Video Time Index in chapter 4; plus the Class Exercises in chapter 6. These provide the key points of the Four Elements method, where they are illustrated on the video, comments and questions to stimulate the group's thinking, and class exercises that demonstrate the principles.

THE ART OF COMPASSIONATE COMMUNICATION

Communicating with compassion is an art, not a science. There is no formula to mechanically go through the motions and then have things work out fine.

Some members of your audience may ask, "Can you tell me what I should say?" There is no such thing as the proper thing to say. There is nothing you can rehearse beforehand that will automatically make people feel better.

Our approach to teaching *Communicating with Compassion* is based on general principles. The Four Elements are four principles of good communication. The more someone understands and practices these principles, the better communicator he will be – in any situation. This is in contrast to having people memorize a list of specific things

"To be successful, the first thing to do is fall in love with your work."

— SISTER MARY LAURETTA

they should or should not do, which, no matter how long the list, would never apply to every situation.

Compassion is the art of being with people during their suffering. The word compassion is derived from the Latin root *compati*: to suffer with. It takes practice, perseverance and humility. But the result will be a new skill and deeper insight into life than you ever had before.

> **Compassion is the art of being with people during their suffering.**

Communicating with Compassion is not a technique you do on someone. Each of the Four Elements is an ingredient. You keep working at it, adding them to your interactions. The more times you put these elements into a conversation, and, the more skillfully you do it – the better the result.

THE PURPOSE OF THE VIDEO

- To inspire compassion and to empower people from all walks of life to make a difference in the lives of others.
- To make volunteer programs more successful through better communication with the people they serve.
- To give lay people the tools to help one another deal with tragedy, illness and distress.
- To strengthen faith, family and community.
- To improve the quality of life for those who suffer alone.
- To get more people involved in visiting those who are in distress – more often and more effectively.

SESSION OVERVIEW

The video can be used in a variety of ways. With a running time of forty minutes, it fits easily within a ninety-minute meeting, with time for a thirty minute discussion, plus opening and closing remarks. The format for such a ninety-minute learning session is described in chapter 2.

For a more in-depth session, you can use the video as the central ingredient in a three-hour workshop, which is described in chapter 3.

First of all we recommend that you watch the video and make notes on any points you may want to comment on. A time index of the video is included in chapter 4 to make it easy to find a particular scene.

The handouts are for your audience, and come with permission to photocopy, so you can make as many copies as necessary without having to order more.

For those who are new to leading workshops, take a look at "Tips for Group Leaders" in chapter 5, for some ideas that make for a successful, memorable session.

YOUR ROLE AS FACILITATOR[2]

As the group leader – the one who is responsible for presenting the videotape and conducting the learning session – your role is also that of a facilitator.

"Blessed are the flexible, for they shall not be bent out of shape."

— ANONYMOUS

A facilitator's role is: **To support everyone to do their best thinking.**

This role was described by the Chinese sage Lao Tzu, when he said, "He leads best when the people say 'we did it ourselves.'"

A facilitator is like a guide. You guide the journey, the process of getting there. You keep the learning process on track, and help the group arrive at the session objectives.

But you don't do the learning for the group. Your concern is more with the process of "how" they get there, rather than the content of "what" they learn. (The content, the subject matter, is already provided by the video.)

Such a learning session is a team effort, and you need the group's participation to succeed. Many people are used to being taught at, and told what to do. They may be unfamiliar with participatory learning. **So it is vitally important to ask your group for their participation.**

You are presenting a different approach – an approach that gives people an opportunity to learn and discover, together.

2 For more information on being a facilitator see the books "How To Make Meetings Work" by Michael Doyle and David Straus, and "Facilitator's Guide to Participatory Decision-Making" by Sam Kaner.

As a facilitator, you are NOT there:

➤ to be, or act as, an expert

➤ to lecture, or tell the group what they should or should not do

➤ to judge, approve or disapprove of their answers

➤ to bias the conversation toward your own interpretation

➤ to do the learning **for** them, or to teach it **to** them – but instead, you are there to work **with** them in the learning process

You ARE there:

➤ to ask the questions that guide the conversation toward the stated goals; and to prompt the group and model the answers if necessary

➤ to keep the conversation on track, by staying with the **process** of asking a series of questions

➤ to encourage everyone to participate

➤ to prevent anyone from dominating the conversation

➤ to make sure that everyone is heard

➤ to allow a free exchange of ideas

➤ to make sure that no one is criticized or attacked

➤ to treat everyone like an adult, with respect

➤ to allow differences of opinion to exist, and not to try to resolve them – but know this: learning is most effective when people share their observations, experiences, insights or decisions, rather than their opinions.

In a nutshell: practice what you preach. You will succeed as a facilitator if you use the Four Elements of compassionate communication shown in the video.

The Four Elements of attention, acknowledgment, affection and acceptance, all encourage participation. After all, when someone takes an interest in what you have to say, don't you feel more inclined to participate?

You know you are succeeding when everyone participates. You know you have succeeded when people leave the session with a newfound enthusiasm for learning about life, and a desire to use the Four Elements to bring compassion into the lives of others.

You will succeed as a facilitator if you use the Four Elements of compassionate communication shown in the video.

NINETY-MINUTE SESSION

NINETY-MINUTE SESSION

2

BEFORE THE SESSION

Before attempting to lead a discussion or workshop we recommend watching the video all the way through – twice. First watch as an observer, as your audience will, gathering first impressions and a sense of the overall flow and content of the video.

Before you see the video for the second time read chapters 2, 3 and 4. Make note of the questions that guide the discussions, and the points that are made in each segment of the video.

Then watch the video a second time with these questions in mind; watching to see where teaching points are made. In this way you will gain greater command of the content, and know more clearly where and when to bring certain points to the audience's attention.

Rather than simply telling the group what they should do, you can guide them toward greater understanding by asking questions that will make them think about a certain point.

For example, to stimulate some thoughts about the importance of paying attention, you could ask, "What kind of body language did the elderly African-American lady use to indicate that she wasn't really up for a visit?" "What would be likely to happen if the visitor hadn't noticed this?"

Because the video shows real life interactions, it is rich with many examples of using, or not using, the Four Elements. Many of the scenes show good examples of two, three or four of the elements – within seconds of each other. You may find a scene in the acknowledgment segment that shows how a lack of affection impacts the patient (there are two.)

In real life, the Four Elements are not used in isolation, but are combined in a variety of ways, appropriate to the situation. This is the art of communicating with compassion.

SESSION TIMELINE

➤ Opening remarks	5 min.
➤ Opening questions	10 min.
➤ Video	40 min.
➤ Discussion	30 min.
➤ Closing remarks	2 min.
➤ Handouts and evaluation forms given out	

OPENING REMARKS (5 min.)

Before showing the video, make sure you introduce yourself and the video[3]. Prepare the audience by:

- *Welcoming them to the session.* Remember: the subject matter you are introducing is warm and friendly, not formal or clinical. Put your audience at ease, help people feel welcome.
- *Explaining your role as facilitator.* A facilitator is someone who guides the session. You are not expected to be an expert on the subject, but to guide the discussion in a way that helps people do their best thinking. (For more information on how to do this see the section " Your Role as Facilitator" in chapter 1.)
- *Presenting the session timeline (for the 90-minute or 3-hour session.)* It is important that your audience knows what they are about to do. The timeline is listed above. You can type it up and hand it out, but it's easier to write it on a flip chart and point it out to the audience during your introduction. Adapt the timeline to meet your needs.
- *Telling why you want them to see the video.* Think about this. Why do you want them to see it? Explain your reasons as clearly as possible, relating your rationale to the next point – the benefits to be gained.
- *Reviewing the possible benefits they will gain.* Describe what's in it for them, for the organization, and for the people they assist. Why should they

> *"There is something I do before I start a session. I let myself know that I am enough. Not perfect. Perfect wouldn't be enough. But that I am human, and that is enough."*
>
> – RACHEL NAOMI REMEN, M.D. DESCRIBING HOW CARL ROGERS WOULD APPROACH A THERAPEUTIC ENCOUNTER.

---

3 Also see Sample Introduction on next page.

spend their time in this session? What will result from it?

- *Disclosing how the video has been useful to you, and/ or why you like it.* Put yourself through the learning process first. Make it work for you. Gain some insight into the value of these skills first-hand.
- *Telling a story that leads to the video.* It's preferable to tell a personal story. It will connect you with your audience.

It's a good idea to sit down ahead of time, and write down your responses to the points mentioned above. If you're nervous, have your notes with you when you begin the session, and go through them point by point.

"We ourselves must be full of life if we are going to make life fuller for others."

– David Sawyer

SAMPLE INTRODUCTION

Here is an example of how a group leader might introduce the session, and lead into the opening discussion:

"Hello, my name is John Rayborn, and I want to thank you for attending this session. What we're about to do is watch a video entitled, *Communicating with Compassion.*

The video is forty-minutes long, and it's designed for professionals and volunteers who are on the front lines – people like you, who are directly helping those who are ill, injured, dying, or in some kind of distress.

The video uses real life interactions, to illustrate four key elements of communicating with compassion. It shows the listening skills that bring hope and lift the spirit.

Then, after watching the video, we'll spend thirty minutes discussing what you've seen and heard.

Here is the timeline for today's session (pointing to the timeline written out on the flip chart.) As you can see, at the end of the session I'll be giving you some handouts that summarize the key learning points we cover today.

My role in all of this is to guide the session – to be your facilitator. I'm not an expert in this subject, so I won't be teaching in the traditional sense. I won't be telling you what you should and shouldn't do. And I don't have to, because the people who really know the subject are in the video. My job as a facilitator is to guide the learning process and help this group to do its best thinking.

In the discussion that follows the video, I'll be asking you a series of questions. The questions are simply a way to structure the discussion, so that we can learn about the subject together. I'm going to need everyone's involvement in the discussion for it to work. So please add your insights as we go along.

Also, as a facilitator, I won't judge, grade, or evaluate any of your answers. This is a creative learning session. The idea is to explore and discover new material together. It's not a test.

I'm excited about showing you this video. It's a new approach to learning about communication. And I'm impressed by the way they've used real staff, volunteers and hospital patients, in real and challenging situations.

It's also been inspiring for me. The video makes it easy to see how much difference we can make in someone's life, just by listening carefully, and by taking an interest in what is important to them.

I think you'll get a lot out of the video because it relates to both our personal and professional lives. The kind of communication skills we're going to see and talk about can make a big difference to our organization's ability to serve its clients. When we apply these skills, we improve not only the client's appreciation for our efforts, but our own job satisfaction as well.

It reminds me of the time I saw a lady in the waiting room while I was rushing through in a hurry to get somewhere. She looked really lost and confused, so I asked her if I could help. In the course of the conversation, just a few questions really, I found out that she knew my mother. They went to elementary school together. She was overjoyed to find someone she could relate to in an unfamiliar environment. And I felt like I made a new friend. It made my day.

"Enthusiasm is always inspirational."

— SISTER PARISH

Before we watch the video, I'd like to get to know you, and give you the chance to get to know one another. I'd like to go around the room and ask you to do two things. First give your name, and second, name a person, or a group of people, who symbolize compassion for you.

For example: "My name is John Rayborn, and a person who symbolizes compassion for me is my mother, Julia Rayborn."

Now let's go around the room. Dorothy, would you go first?"

OPENING QUESTIONS (10 min.)

No matter how well you know the members of your audience, there are some important questions to ask before you begin. These questions prepare the way for a successful session, by creating a context in which to show the video. Without this context, if you just show the video "cold," it will be more difficult for your audience to learn. These questions also help everyone feel included and involved, and make for a better discussion afterwards.

PURPOSE:
The reason for the opening discussion is for the audience to understand the context and purpose of the session:

➤ to relate what they are about to see to their past experience;

➤ to get in touch with the benefits of compassionate listening;

➤ and to feel included, involved and ready to learn something new.

OPENING QUESTIONS:

Go around the room and ask each member of the audience to respond to the first two questions (if time and the size of your group permits). But first, model the answers for the group, by doing it yourself.

1   Give your name.

2   Name a person (or an organization) who symbolizes compassion for you.

Now ask:

3   Who here has ever been seriously ill, in distress, or badly needed someone's help? (Or: Have you ever had to depend on the kindness of strangers?) (Ask for a show of hands. As the facilitator, you should also raise your own, if it applies to you.)

4   How many have been in the opposite situation, where you didn't know what to say or how to act around someone who was suffering? (Show of hands.)

5   Who has ever put his foot in his mouth, in a sensitive situation? (Show of hands.)

6   What do you hope to gain from today's session? (Or: What is important to you about today's topic?)

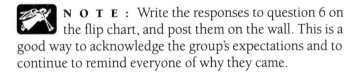 **N O T E :** Write the responses to question 6 on the flip chart, and post them on the wall. This is a good way to acknowledge the group's expectations and to continue to remind everyone of why they came.

Before asking question 6, make sure that people know why they are attending. Even if you have to point to the announcement poster (see handouts pocket), or preface question 6 with, "Since we're here to focus on how to communicate with compassion… "

Now you are ready to show the video.

TIPS ON SHOWING THE VIDEO

Make sure that you check out the room and the equipment ahead of time. See the "Leader's Checklist" in chapter 4 for details. Play the first minute or so of the video before people arrive to make sure the picture and sound are set correctly. (It helps to have someone nearby who knows how to adjust the tracking, color balance and sound levels.)

If you plan on using the video time index (in chapter 4) to cue the video to specific scenes, reset the VCR's time counter to read zero as the program begins. This way, the time stated in the index will correspond to the time on your VCR.

Make sure that everyone can see and hear the TV, and that they are comfortable enough to sit for forty minutes. Glare on the screen or in the audience's eyes is the most common problem. Find out ahead of time where to pull the blinds or curtains, and where to dim the lights.

A dim (but not totally dark) room is preferable for showing the video. Remember to bring the lights back up, or open the curtains, after the show. The discussion should be held under good lighting conditions, where everyone can see each other's expressions.

If the TV screen is too small for your group, the people at the back will be frustrated by not being able to see or hear. Generally a 13 inch screen is good for a group of no more than six. A 19 inch screen is fine for up to 20. For up to 30 you'll need a 27 inch, and for more than that it's best to use several monitors or a big screen projection TV. Try to arrange your class size or equipment accordingly.

During the show, try to minimize distractions. Quiet, well-ventilated, 68° F, rooms are optimal. And don't be too shy to hang a "Do Not Disturb: Seminar in Progress" sign on the door.

If you know a latecomer is going to arrive, meet them by the doorway, indicate "quiet please," and lead them to an empty chair – at the back of the group.

"It is best for men, when they take counsel, to be timorous, and imagine all possible calamities, but when the time for action comes, then to deal boldly."

— HERODOTUS

A good seating arrangement for viewing the video, and for the discussion, is a U-shaped or semicircular arrangement. This way there is a natural focus on the group leader and on the TV, and it also allows people to see and talk to one another. After viewing the video, if it's not too distracting, you could close up the open end of the U-shape or semi-circle, to make a full circle for the discussion.

The Payoff:
Actions really do speak louder than words, and by taking the time to cover all of these details, you send a very powerful unspoken message: "This work is important!" More than anything you can say, this message sets the stage for success.

DISCUSSING THE VIDEO (30 min.)

For more details on the method used to develop this discussion, read "The Discussion Method" in the appendix.

DISCUSSION PURPOSE:

The purpose of this conversation is to give the audience an opportunity to reflect on the video:

➤ to gain deeper insight into compassion and communication;

➤ to discover at least one way to improve one's ability to communicate;

➤ to get to touch with the feeling behind compassionate communication;

➤ to be motivated to put the Four Elements into practice.

NOTE: Be aware that some members of the audience may be deeply moved by the video. As a result, the group may be very quiet and slow in getting started. You will need to be patient, and sensitive to their need to regain composure.

The closing song, during the credits, is very helpful in this regard. Allowing people to just sit and listen as the credits roll, is a good way to give them time to collect themselves and think about what they have seen, before engaging in a discussion.

Having a box (or two) of tissues, tactfully placed in the room, is another considerate gesture that will help some members of the audience regain their composure.

DISCUSSION QUESTIONS:

Begin the discussion by giving a one-sentence overview of what you are about to do. For example: "Now we're going to discuss our reactions to the video."

Then ask the following questions (in this order.)

1 What moment or scene stands out for you?

2 What was said that stuck with you? (Ask everyone to speak to at least one of the first two questions.)

3 Which of the Four Elements of *Communicating with Compassion* do you remember? (As people name them, write the Four Elements on a flip chart. First write the numbers 1 through 4, down the side of the paper, and as people call out the elements, fill in the appropriate space, so they are listed in the order they appear in the video.)

4 How did you feel when you saw people do it all wrong?

5 What feelings did the video leave you with?

6 What was the key point, or most important message, for you? (Or: What did you learn that's new for you?) (Have everyone speak to question #6 if possible.)

7 Which of the Four Elements are you going to pay more attention to the next time you visit with, or help, someone?

8 What is one thing you will do differently to improve the way you communicate? (Or: What is one way you can apply these principles of compassionate listening to your particular job or situation?)

As people name them, write the Four Elements on a flip chart.

N O T E : Go around the room and get a comment from everyone on question 8. If the members of your audience do not work or volunteer within a hospital or nursing home, use the alternative question 8, to focus on how these skills are applicable to the specific situations they deal with.

 N O T E : If it's slow going, or if you need to take the discussion deeper, repeat the question, rephrase it, or give an example answer yourself. You know things are going well when the discussion starts to flow and people start to answer your next question before you have asked it.

 N O T E : To increase participation in larger groups, break into smaller groups of three to six people – it feels safer, and everyone gets a chance to speak. Break into small groups after question 3, and have them discuss questions 4 through 6. Then reconvene the whole group for questions 7 & 8.

 N O T E : In all of the discussions in this Leader Guide, there are one or two questions where we suggest hearing from everyone in the group. This is important because it shares the responsibility of learning together, and it increases the probability that members will retain and implement the material. But for very large groups, this may be impossible. So adapt the session accordingly.

CLOSING REMARKS

Conclude the discussion by doing a recap of what was discussed. If you have someone take notes, it makes it easier to recap; and if you posted the notes on the wall, you can point to them so that everyone can see the fruits of their discussion. (See "Timekeeping & Chartwriting" in chap. 5.)

Another way to conclude the session is to summarize the key points that you want group members to remember from the video. Make a list of these points beforehand, and have them written up on the flip chart for easy reference. The Video Time Index in chapter 4, will help you find the scenes where these points are demonstrated.

The deepest

principle in human

nature is

the craving to be

appreciated.

– WILLIAM JAMES

N O T E : *If your group remembers only one thing about the video,* this point is the most important: **Always ask permission** before you visit with, or help, someone. Give the person you wish to assist, a choice – and honor that choice.

This simple act, of asking permission, restores a sense of control to a person who is probably feeling that he has little control. (Why else would he need your help?) And this builds rapport (because he knows that you will listen to, and respond to, his wishes.) In this way, your interaction always sets out on the right foot.

The end of the session is the best time to give out the hand-outs on the Four Elements, which are a reminder of the experience, as well as a handy reference for the material you covered. Include with the handouts an evaluation form, and ask for the group's comments on the session. This will help you make your next session even better.

Most importantly, warmly thank everyone for their participation. Learning together is a team effort – you can't do it without them.

Ideas won't keep.

Something must be

done about them.

— ALFRED NORTH
   WHITEHEAD

THREE-HOUR WORKSHOP

3

*T*HREE-HOUR WORKSHOP

3

After taking a ten-minute break, come back and discuss each of the Four Elements one at a time.

 N O T E : To use the *Communicating with Compassion* video as the basis for a three-hour workshop, **first conduct the ninety-minute session described in chapter 2,** except for giving out the handouts and making the closing remarks.

Then, after taking a ten-minute break, come back and discuss each of the Four Elements one at a time. The format for discussing each element is basically the same: review the video segment on that element, and then hold a 10-minute discussion. Then repeat this format with the next element.

🕐 SESSION TIMELINE

Part 1 (85 min.: same format as 90-minute session)
                                                      begin after:
- ➤ Opening remarks: 5 min.
- ➤ Opening discussion: 10 min.   5 min.
- ➤ Video: 40 min.   15 min.
- ➤ Discussion: 30 min.   55 min.
- ➤ Break instructions: 1 min.   85 min. (1:25)

Break (9 min.)   86 min. (1:26)

Part 2 (85-min.)
- ➤ Part 2 opening remarks (2 min)   95 min. (1:35)
- ➤ Attention (6 min. of video)   97 min. (1:37)
  10-minute discussion
- ➤ Acknowledgment (9 min. of video) 113 min.
  (1:53)
  10-minute discussion
- ➤ Affection (3 min. of video)   132 min. (2:12)
  10-minute discussion
- ➤ Acceptance (8 min. of video)   145 min. (2:26)
  10-minute discussion
- ➤ Concluding discussion (15 min.)   163 min. (2:44)
- ➤ Closing remarks: 2 min.   178 min. (2:58)
- ➤ Handouts and evaluation forms given out

USING LONGER BREAKS

If you have an extra hour, you can make the session into a four-hour workshop by using the break to go out and visit some residents in a nursing home, or visit some elderly people you know. Then return to the classroom and revisit the Four Elements. You and your audience will find the discussions far more meaningful and rewarding, after experiencing the subject first-hand.

Alternatively, split the session into two parts. On the first day, conduct the ninety-minute session as outlined in chapter 2. Then between sessions have the class gain some experience assisting people in need. Then at the second session, say the following week, conduct the second part of the three-hour workshop.

Before leading these discussions, review "Listening Skills that Build Participation" in chapter 5.

Attention

ATTENTION REVIEW & DISCUSSION

16 min. (6:00 min. of video plus 10 min. of discussion)

First write the discussion title, ATTENTION at the top of a flip chart. Underneath it write the definition of paying attention:

> ATTENTION
> Being aware of the signs, signals and clues that indicate what is important to someone.

Now replay the Attention segment of the video.

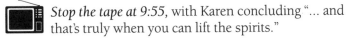

Start the video at 3:55 (from the beginning,) just prior to the definition of Attention, when Karen summarizes the Four Elements beginning with, "Each and everyone of us here has been touched by someone's death, someone's illness..."

Stop the tape at 9:55, with Karen concluding "... and that's truly when you can lift the spirits."

DISCUSSION PURPOSE:

➤ to gain a deeper understanding of why paying attention improves one's ability to interact with people in need.

➤ to discover at least one way to improve the way one pays attention.

➤ to get a sense of what it is like to be aware of the signs, signals and clues that indicate what is important to someone.

DISCUSSION QUESTIONS:

After playing the video segment on Attention, ask the following questions:

1 What example of paying attention did you see in the video?

2 What is another way to describe paying attention? (Or: What is paying attention all about? What are some key words?)

3 How did you feel when you heard patients talk about their situations? (Or: How would you feel if you were in Dale Brothers' shoes?)

4 What does it feel like when people pay attention to you?

5 What have you experienced when you failed to pay attention?

6 What blocks us from being aware of what is important to someone? (What gets in the way? Why don't we notice?) (Ask everyone to answer question 6.)

7 How will you pay attention differently in the future? (Or: How can you apply the principle of paying attention to your communication? In the situations you deal with?) (Ask everyone to answer question 7.)

N O T E : The questions in parentheses are essentially the same as the question they follow. They are just rephrased to elicit more responses, in case the first way you stated the question didn't bring enough answers. As you gain experience guiding these discussions, you'll come up with your own wording for these questions, to best suit the needs of your group.

However, as you adapt the questions, read about the four types of questions in "The Discussion Method" (see appendix). Make sure the objective questions stay objective, and the reflective ones, reflective, etc.

 N O T E : To increase participation in larger groups, break into smaller groups (of 3-6 people.) Again, it helps participants feel more at ease, and gives everyone a chance to speak. In the discussion on Attention, above, break into small groups for questions 3, 4 & 5. In the other discussions break into small groups as follows:

Acknowledgment – for questions 3 & 4
Affection – for questions 3 & 4
Acceptance – for questions 3, 4, 5 & 6

KEY LEARNING STRATEGIES
for the discussion on Attention on page 26

Stay with question 2 (What is another way to describe paying attention?) until some of the words and phrases listed below have been mentioned.

➤ Listening Seeing Feeling
➤ Asking permission (to enter, visit, help, support).
➤ Giving choices, giving control; e.g. "Is this a good time for me to visit?"
➤ Accepting his answer, whether yes or no.
➤ Observing the subtleties in a person's body language, tone of voice, facial expressions.
➤ Responding to her signals; following her lead.
➤ Going with what he wants to talk about, or discuss.
➤ Recognizing what is appreciated, and what isn't.
➤ Focusing on what is right with a person, rather than what's wrong.

"I believe the greatest gift I can conceive of having from anyone, is to be seen by them, heard by them and touched by them. And the greatest gift that I can give is to see, hear, understand and touch another person. When this is done, contact is made."

– Virginia Satir

If the group is slow in getting started, or if they seem to get stuck on a particular question, prompt them by giving some of the answers above. *As answers are called out, write them down underneath the definition of Attention.*

The idea is to explore the many aspects of paying attention, and to get the group in touch with how they can become more "aware of the signs, signals and clues that indicate what is important to someone."

You can also prompt the group by asking questions, such as:
> ➤ "What did the doctor say was the most important thing someone could do for a patient?" (A: Listen to them.)
> ➤ "What did the high school girl do before entering the patient's room?" (A: Asked permission to enter.)

(See the "Video Time Index" in chapter 4 for more ideas.)

The idea is to explore the many aspects of paying attention.

At the end of the discussion on Attention, tear off the sheet of paper on which you have written the definition and key words, and tape it on the wall. It then functions as part of the "group memory" – a reminder for the rest of the session.

Stay with question #6 (What blocks us from being aware of what is important to someone?) until some of the following points have been mentioned. As with question 2, prompt the group by giving some of the answers listed below. *Unlike question 2, don't write the answers down.*
> ➤ Following your own agenda instead of her lead.
> ➤ Not asking permission.
> ➤ Not giving any choices, or a sense of control.
> ➤ Intruding, interrupting, controlling.
> ➤ Getting caught up in your own feelings, opinions and needs.
> ➤ Focusing only on what you are doing to her, or doing for her, but avoiding being with her.
> ➤ Making assumptions
> ➤ Assuming the worst. Assuming the best.
> ➤ Assuming he wants your help, or your company.
> ➤ Never asking questions to check that you understood.
> ➤ Ignoring the signals, being insensitive.

> Ignoring signs on the door.
> Never noticing how someone is feeling.

The idea is to explore the ways in which we stop ourselves from noticing what is important to the people we assist.

Acknowledgment

The greatest good

you can do for

another is not just to

share your riches

but to reveal to him

his own.

— Benjamin Disraeli

ACKNOWLEDGMENT REVIEW & DISCUSSION
19 min. (9 min. of video plus 10 min. of discussion)

Each of the four discussions on the Four Elements follows the same format. As with the discussion on Attention, first write the discussion title at the top of a new page on the flip chart. Underneath it write the definition:

> ACKNOWLEDGMENT
> Letting someone know that you recognize
> and appreciate him as a unique individual.

Now play the Acknowledgment segment of the video.

 Start the tape at 10:45, with the definition of Acknowledgment (over the background of a blue landscape.)

 Stop the tape at 19:25, after Sam Leer, Director of Medical Social Services, says "...a life well lived." (Before the story about Ethiopia.)

 DISCUSSION PURPOSE:
> to gain a better understanding of how acknowledgment can improve one's ability to communicate with people in need.
> to discover at least one new way to acknowledge people.
> to get a sense of what it is like to let someone know that you recognize and appreciate them as a unique individual.

DISCUSSION QUESTIONS:

After playing the video segment on acknowledgment, ask the following questions:

1 What is an example of acknowledgment that you saw in the video?

2 What is another way to describe acknowledgment? (Or: What is acknowledgment all about? Give me some key words or phrases.)

3 How does it feel when someone acknowledges you?

4 How would you feel if you were one of the patients in the "blooper" scene?

5 What do people do instead of acknowledging each other?

6 What happens when you acknowledge people?

7 In what different ways can you acknowledge someone?

8 Regarding acknowledgment, or the lack of it – name one thing you will do differently? (Or: How can you add the element of acknowledgment to the work or service that you do?)
(Get a response from everyone on question 8.)

 KEY LEARNING STRATEGIES
for the discussion on Acknowledgment above

Stay with question 2 (What is another way to describe acknowledgment?) until some of the following have been mentioned:

➤ Appreciation. Respect.
➤ Taking a genuine interest in the person.
➤ Asking good questions.
➤ Talking about what's special, important or interesting, to him.
➤ Helping people feel needed, wanted and valued.
➤ Commenting on how she has made a difference.
➤ Recognizing abilities, qualities and strengths.
➤ Validation, affirmation.

Again, you can prompt the audience by giving some of these key words and phrases. As these answers are called out, write them under the definition of Acknowledgment.

This helps the group explore the various attributes of Acknowledgment, and gain insight into how they can "let someone know that you recognize and appreciate them as a unique individual."

The following kinds of questions can also draw a response:

➤ How did Karen acknowledge the female patient she visited, while she was wearing a mask? (Did you notice how they managed to have a warm, uplifting conversation – despite the fact that they were total strangers, Karen was wearing a mask, and the lady had leukemia? Not to mention the presence of a video camera in the room.)

➤ In the story the priest told about his visit with the man who may have been unconscious, what did he talk about that caused the man to shed a tear?

➤ When the Oncology nurse talked about his experience of being in the Intensive Care Unit, what did he say had the biggest impact on his recovery?

At the end of the discussion on Acknowledgment, tear off the sheet of paper on which you have written the definition and key words, and tape it on the wall, next to the one on Attention. You are continuing to build the "group memory."

Prompting the group by giving them some of the answers, can help to jump start the conversation. But if you do it too often, the group will be tempted to let you do their thinking for them, and you'll loose their participation.

Stay with question #5 (What do people do instead of acknowledging each other?) until some of the following points have been mentioned. Your focus is to help the group discover the different ways in which we avoid acknowledging people.

➤ Give advice: "What you really need to do is think positive."

➤ Invalidate/discount/deny someone's feelings,

Advice is seldom welcome, and those who need it the most, like it the least.

– Lord Chesterfield

perspective or experience: "You shouldn't worry about that."
➤ Be condescending: "There, there, it'll be all right."
➤ Use cliches: "It could have been worse." "Every cloud has a silver lining."
➤ Use one-upmanship: "This is nothing, you should have seen Fred when it happened to him."
➤ Tell your tale of woe: " I was in labor for 48 hours – you've never felt such pain."
➤ Tell horror stories: "The doctor told me that this is the worst case he's ever seen."

Again, if necessary, prompt the group with questions such as: How did the young girl who visited the lady patient in the "blooper scene" make the patient feel worse?

Affection

AFFECTION REVIEW & DISCUSSION
13 min. (3 min. of video plus 10 min. of discussion)

Write the definition of affection on the top of a new piece of paper:

> **AFFECTION**
> **the human touch of warmth,**
> **comfort, humor and kindness.**

Start the video at 23:20, which begins with the definition of affection (over the background of a heart monitor.)

Stop the tape at 26:35, after Kelley, the high school volunteer says, "...I really touched somebody's life today, and maybe vice versa, someone touched mine. " (Before the ocean and the Acceptance definition.)

 DISCUSSION PURPOSE:
➤ to gain a better understanding of why affection can improve one's ability to communicate with people in need.
➤ to discover at least one new way to show affection to people.
➤ to get a sense of what it is like to give the human touch of warmth, comfort, humor and kindness.

DISCUSSION QUESTIONS:

After playing the video segment on affection, ask the following questions:

1 What is an example of affection that you saw in the video?

2 What is another way of describing affection? (Or: What is affection all about?)

3 If you are going through a difficult situation, what kind of affection helps you feel cared about?

4 What did the doctor's story about the Hopi Indian mean to you?

5 How do we act when we choose not to be friendly or caring?

6 In what ways can you show affection to someone in distress?

7 In what way will you approach affection differently? (Or: How can you apply the principle of showing affection appropriately to your communication? In the situations you deal with?)

(Go around the room on question 7, and get a response from everyone.)

 KEY LEARNING STRATEGIES
for the discussion on Affection above

Remember your role as a facilitator: to help the group do their best thinking. In this case it's to help them discover more ways to show affection.

Stay with question 2 (What is another way of describing affection?) until some of the following have been mentioned, prompting when necessary:

➤ Finding common ground.

➤ Sharing.

➤ Being together.

➤ Warmth. Comfort. Kindness.

The Eskimo has fifty-two names for snow, because it is important to them; there ought to be as many for love.

– MARGARET ATWOOD

> ➤ Thoughtful. Considerate.
> ➤ Appropriate use of touch.
> ➤ Heart, joy, good humor.
> ➤ Smiles.

Some questions that could stimulate thinking about affection:

> ➤ Why was Dale (the patient) open to receive a hug from Kelley (the student volunteer) even though they had known each other for about 20 minutes, and he had initially been hesitant to let her visit with him?
> ➤ Why might some people be afraid of hugs?

"...in every gesture

dignity and love. "

– John Milton

Write the key words that the group came up with, under the definition of affection, and hang the sheet on the wall next to the others covering attention and acknowledgment.

Stay with question #5 (How do we behave when we choose not to be friendly or caring?) until some of the following points have been mentioned. This lack of affection is also demonstrated in the blooper scene, by the older couple who visit, and the young man who stands over the bed.

> ➤ Showing no warmth, no feelings, no empathy.
> ➤ Being distant and aloof.
> ➤ Taking yourself too seriously.
> ➤ Finding no common ground.
> ➤ Staring, or its opposite, no eye contact.
> ➤ Talking about her as if she were an object, a body, or as if she were not in the same room.
> ➤ Talking down to someone, being condescending.

Acceptance

ACCEPTANCE REVIEW & DISCUSSION

17-18 min. (7.5 min. of video plus 10 min. of discussion)

Write the definition of acceptance at the top of a new sheet on your flip chart:

> ACCEPTANCE
> **Allowing things to be the way they are**

Start the video at 26:38, and play the acceptance segment of the video, which begins with the definition of acceptance (over the background of the ocean.)

Stop the tape at 34:03, after the nurse, says "...and we shouldn't pretend we know the answers. " (Before the black & white image of Karen walking into the hospital.)

DISCUSSION PURPOSE:

➤ to gain a better understanding of how acceptance can improve one's ability to communicate with people in need.

➤ to discover at least one new way to be accepting of people.

➤ to get a sense of what it is like to allow things to be the way they are.

 ### DISCUSSION QUESTIONS:

After playing the video segment on Acceptance, ask the following questions:

1 What are some examples of acceptance that you saw in the video?
2 What is another way to describe acceptance?
3 How did you feel when you saw the men crying?
4 How does it feel when people don't accept you?
5 What does it mean to be accepting?
6 What blocks us from accepting a situation?
7 What do we do when we are not being accepting?
8 What are some ways you can show acceptance to someone?
9 What new way of accepting people will you add? (Or: How can you add the element of acceptance to the work or service that you perform?)
(Go around the room and get an answer from everyone on this question.)

NOTE ABOUT ACCEPTANCE: Some people may object to the concept of acceptance on the grounds that we shouldn't be resigned to our fate and just do nothing. This is not the form of acceptance we mean.

The situations we are describing are ones in which the caregiver is not in a position to change the situation – to cure a person of cancer, or to make an injury go away, for example. These are sometimes the facts of life.

It is the job of the professionals in the field, such as doctors or social workers, to work toward a remedy for the situation. But we, as lay people, can do a great deal to help others cope – by accepting them, and the challenges set before them.

 KEY LEARNING STRATEGIES
for the discussion on Acceptance on page 35

Acceptance is the most abstract of the Four Elements, and it is also the most emotional segment of the video. So it is all the more important for you, as facilitator, to keep the discussion focused.

Stay with question 2 (What is another way to describe acceptance?) until some of the following facets of acceptance have been mentioned:

➤ Helping people feel safe and comfortable with you.
➤ Non-judgmental.
➤ No pretenses.
➤ Faith.
➤ Humility. Being willing to say "I don't know."
➤ Open. Non-grasping. Open to change.
➤ Letting go of wanting it to be a certain way.
➤ Letting it be all right, as it is.
➤ Giving permission to speak freely.
➤ Giving permission to express feelings.
➤ Universal Love. Agape.

Some questions that will stimulate the audience's thinking about acceptance:

➤ What did the nurse say we shouldn't do?
(A: pretend to have the answers.)

Everything in life

that we really

accept undergoes a

change. So suffering

must become Love.

That is the mystery.

– Katherine Mansfield

➤ Why did the director of nursing say volunteers are so valuable? (A: because they can spend quality time, and help people feel cared about.)

➤ What was important to the man who had a stroke, who cried? (A: his family, his work, the compassion of the nurses.)

➤ What was Richard, the bald man who cried, really talking about when he said, "I'm going home."? (A: his imminent death.)

➤ Why did these men feel safe to express their deepest feelings? (A: the visitors listened, acknowledged them, showed affection appropriately, and accepted them, and what they were going through.)

Write the group's responses on your flip chart, the same way you did in the previous discussions. Then hang the sheet on the wall with the others.

Stay with question #7 (What do we do when we are not being accepting?) until some of the following points have been mentioned:

➤ Pretend that the situation is different from the way it really is.

➤ Pretend to know the answer when you don't.

➤ Avoiding the difficult issues that people may want to talk about.

➤ Avoid the obvious or the inevitable.

➤ Try to rescue people from their problems.

➤ Try to fix it, change it, or make it all better.

➤ Be judgmental, critical, sarcastic, cynical, bitter.

➤ Get irritated, complain, blame everyone, find fault with everything.

➤ Be indifferent, blasé … "whatever".

➤ Get defensive, take it personally, be inflexible.

➤ Lay guilt trips: "If only you had listened to me this never would have happened."

"Everything has its wonders, even darkness and silence."

– HELEN KELLER

CLOSING DISCUSSION (15 min.)

You are now ready to wrap-up the session. No more notes are necessary. The group memory is on the wall to serve as a reminder of the points you covered, and the discoveries you've made, during the workshop.

 THE REASON FOR THE CLOSING DISCUSSION IS:

➤ to summarize the whole experience.

➤ to prepare to apply the *Communicating with Compassion* principles in the real world.

➤ for the participants to feel confident about trying out new ways of communicating.

"Ain't nothin' to it

but to do it."

— MAYA ANGELOU

DISCUSSION QUESTIONS:

1 From the video or the discussions we've had today, what do you remember most? (Go around the room. Get a response from everyone on this question.)

2 How has this session changed the way you feel about communicating with people in need?

3 In the light of what we've learned in this session, what will be most challenging for you?

4 Who has a situation coming up where you'll have an opportunity to apply this? Can you tell the group about the situation, and how you intend to apply this?

5 How do you see these principles making a difference in your personal or work relationships?
(It's important to get a response from everyone in the room, on question 5, the final question of the day.)

CLOSING REMARKS

Now is the best time to pass out the handouts. The handouts give the audience some ready-made notes about the Four Elements, and serve as a future reference for the main points covered in the workshop.

Include with the handouts an evaluation form, and ask for feedback on the session. This will help you make your next session even better.

 NOTE: If your group remembers only one thing about the video, this point is the most important: Always ask permission before you visit with, or help, someone. Give the person you wish to assist, a choice – and honor that choice.

This simple act, of asking permission, restores a sense of control to a person who is probably feeling that he has little control. (Why else would he need your help?) And this builds trust (because he knows that you will listen, and respond to his wishes.) In this way, your interaction always sets out on the right foot.

Most importantly, warmly thank everyone for their participation.

Always ask permission before you visit with, or help, someone.

BACKGROUND MATERIAL

BACKGROUND MATERIAL

4

GROUP LEADER'S CHECKLIST

- ❏ VCR (VHS format).
- ❏ TV (big enough for everyone to see and hear).
- ❏ Videotape, *Communicating with Compassion*, rewound and ready to go.
- ❏ Room: quiet, comfortable, well-ventilated, free from distractions.
- ❏ No glare on the TV screen or in the audience's eyes.
- ❏ Know how to dim the lights.
- ❏ "Do not disturb/seminar in progress" sign on door.
- ❏ Handouts photocopied, enough for everyone. Originals put back in folder for next time.
- ❏ Flip chart easel, paper & marker pens.
- ❏ Masking tape.
- ❏ Choose the wall on which you will hang the sheets of flip chart paper.
- ❏ Box(es) of Kleenex tissues.
- ❏ Sense of humor.
- ❏ Announcements/invitations have gone out; people know why they're attending.
- ❏ Have a good idea of who will be attending.
- ❏ Have anticipated some of their questions, interests and expectations.
- ❏ Goals for the session are clear.
- ❏ Session length and format decided on.
- ❏ Have viewed the video and know which scenes you want to comment on.
- ❏ Have read the Leader Guide and reviewed the handouts.
- ❏ Discussion questions are prepared.
- ❏ Extra questions and other material prepared, if applicable.
- ❏ Know exactly how you will begin and end this session.
- ❏ Have prepared your introduction.

■ VIDEO TIME INDEX

Here is a list of events that happen in the video that can be used to illustrate or emphasize specific learning points. First, be sure to let your audience see the video all the way through without any pauses. Then revisit the scenes you want to comment on, using this time index as a guide.

TIME ON VIDEO	SCENE	COMMENTS/LEARNING POINTS
0:37	Opening remarks by Karen Fox	*"If you're motivated to reach out… no expectations… that's the key…"*
1:12	Volunteers share why they get involved.	*"It's such a wonderful feeling… it stays with you for life." "You get food for your soul." "I have fun." "We were relating… as two friends."* Why do you get involved in helping others? What are some rewarding moments you've experienced?
1:54	Adventures in Caring and Raggedy montage.	About the Adventures in Caring Foundation and the Raggedy Ann & Andy Visiting Programs.
2:48	Doctor and social services director, interview.	*"Medical intervention may be less important than the psychological or emotional support, provided by family, friends, good listeners…" "Nurses don't have the time to practice nursing as it was practiced 30 or 40 years ago… when they had time… to have that heart-to-heart interaction."* What changes have you noticed in your work (in health care or human services) over the last few years? How do these changes affect the emotional support given to people in need?
3:25	Black & white hospital montage.	*"Visitors find hospitals to be really frightening places…"* To people who are not familiar with hospitals, this scene shows how intimidating it can appear. What is it about your organization that can intimidate or confuse the people it serves?
3:55	Karen Fox summarizes the Four Elements of *Communicating with Compassion*	*"Every one of us has been touched by someone's death, someone's illness… so how can you be of the greatest support? Four elements: Attention, Acknowledgment, Affection and Acceptance."* Who here has wondered what to say to someone who is suffering? Which of the four elements do you remember? Why are these four elements important? (A: Because they meet four basic human needs.)

TIME ON VIDEO	SCENE	COMMENTS/LEARNING POINTS
4:35	**ATTENTION** definition	*Being aware of the signs, signals and clues that indicate what is important to someone.*
4:40	Oncology doctor in scrubs	*"The most important thing any visitor in the room can do, is to be a good listener, and not project your feelings onto the patient."* What did he say is the most important thing anyone can do for a patient?
5:07	Karen listening to lady patient describe her fear of cancer and paralysis.	*"...then I woke up and couldn't move, and one of my biggest fears had come true, again... Before that, cancer was my biggest fear... now I'm paralyzed."* Do you notice what Karen is doing? (A: She's listening. She's not interrupting, feeling sorry, or telling the patient not to worry.)
5:37	Volunteer enters hospital room. Lady patient is about to have her lunch	*"...May I come in?" "I'm just getting ready to have my lunch." "Would you rather I come back? What would you like?"* What other facial expressions or gestures do people use to indicate what they would like, without saying anything?
6:02	Freeze frame on lady's face. Karen's commentary from classroom.	*"...by her visual expression, what does she really want? Her lunch... but so many people miss that clue when they are not paying attention."* What situations have you been in, where obvious signals were missed?
6:34	Laughter. Visitor leaves.	*"We've got a nice cafeteria here." "O.K. I'll come back."* Here's another classic hint. Who knows people that would have missed both clues — her facial gestures, and the comment about the cafeteria? (No names, please!) Why do they miss the signals?
6:45	High school volunteer (Kelley) knocks on door and asks permission to come in. Then she begins to talk with him.	*"Hi! Are you feeling up for a visit this afternoon?"* Notice how she waits, taking nothing for granted, and makes sure she has the patient's permission before going in. Why is it so important to ask permission to enter? (A: to give a choice; to give some control of the conversation to the patient. This builds rapport immediately.) If your group remembers only one thing about the video, this point is the most important: Always ask permission before you visit with, or help, someone. Give him a choice.

TIME ON VIDEO	SCENE	COMMENTS/LEARNING POINTS
7:00	Karen's commentary on Kelley's entrance.	*"Did you notice how she came in and got down (to eye level) … and her patience with him as he's trying to get the words out."* How does it feel when someone stands over you? Or when people finish your sentences for you? Did you notice the warmth of the interaction – even though this was the very first time these two had met? Why? (A: She's listening carefully, respectfully; and responding to his answers.)
7:37	Kelley listening to him talk about rehabilitation. Then commenting on his name.	*"Does that mean you can leave the hospital soon? "Not for a while" "Jim Brothers? Dale? It's been a pleasure to meet you."*
8:12	Karen comments on the importance of repeating back someone's name.	*"When she first heard him, she didn't get it correctly… people like you to remember their names."*
8:12	Kelley speaking	*"It appears to me that you have a real fighter attitude."*
8:35	Karen's commentary from the classroom.	*"You always want to come from first person… that way the person feels you're genuine."* By speaking in this way, you're describing your own observation. There's no argument about whether it's true or not, it's just your point of view. This saves a lot of time by not getting into disagreements and debates. What's the last thing anyone wants when they're dealing with a crisis? (A: For you to talk down to them, to be condescending.) *"She's acknowledging his fighting spirit. And that's the whole beauty - to help them receive your caring. And that's truly when you can lift the spirit…"*
9:55	Black & white nursing home montage: feet walking down hallway.	*Caption: More than 50% of residents in nursing homes have no visitors.* If you lived in a nursing home, how would you feel if you had no contact with the outside world? What would you want most? How would you want to be treated?

TIME ON VIDEO	SCENE	COMMENTS/LEARNING POINTS
10:45	**ACKNOWLEDG-MENT** definition	*Letting someone know that you recognize and appreciate them as a unique individual.*
11:15	Priest walking through a field, telling a story.	*"… about a week ago I visited a man who had a stroke… I didn't know if he was conscious or not… but I held his hand and talked to him… I spoke about the lives he touched as a coach… I saw a tear coming down from his eye… you never know."* In the story the priest tells, how did he acknowledge the stroke patient he visited? (A: By anointing him, talking to him, holding his hand, talking about the lives he touched – even though the man may be unconscious) How did the man respond?
12:27	Oncology nurse comments on his experience as a patient.	*"…I spent about two and a half weeks in intensive care… a good deal of that time I was unconscious…but I have remembrances of my loved one's faces coming by…it was everything (to me.)"*
13:15	Karen puts on a mask and visits an artist in the hospital	*"… when they discuss certain things… whatever they are talking about when they get that sparkle in their eye… bring that up."* How does Karen acknowledge the artist? (A: talks about her artwork, and looks at it) Do you notice how this puts the artist at ease, and the conversation is friendly – even though Karen has never met her before, and is wearing a mask? (Not to mention that the lady had leukemia and was frightened and in pain.)
13:48	Young man with male patient. Man with elderly lady.	*"I heard you had a wedding." "What did you do in show biz?"* How do these men acknowledge the people they are with? (A: By taking an interest in their lives.)
14:22	Interview with lady volunteer (with hat on.)	*"There are stories these people have to tell… when they're gone, these stories will be gone."*
14:41	Lady patient tells a story about slaves from Africa	*"…they weren't coming over here to be slaves."* Hearing oral history is one of the great benefits of volunteering. What surprising stories have you been told by people you've helped. How did you feel when this lady told her story?

TIME ON VIDEO	SCENE	COMMENTS/LEARNING POINTS
15:10	Volunteer comment	*"It's surprising how much so little can do to make someone's day."*
15:32	Female nursing administrator tells a story about riding in a wheelchair	*"...the single biggest criticism...they never once established eye contact..."* What bothered the patients in the wheelchair? What does this tell you about the need for acknowledgment?
16:10	Male Social Services Director (Sam Leer)	*"...there are some very well meaning individuals who ...sometimes create problems."*
16:22	Blooper scene: young woman visitor.	*"You shouldn't be worried about these kinds of things ... we're doing fine without you"* What did she do wrong? What similar things have you done, or seen others do?
16:49	Blooper scene: older couple visiting.	*"...I got the impression that this was the worst case they'd had in a long time. Maybe it's not so good after all."* Does this sound familiar? What is going wrong here? (Refer to the handouts and chapter 6.)
17:10	Blooper scene: young man visitor standing over bed.	*"I don't see what the big deal is all about...it can't be that bad."* Look at your bloopers list – which mistakes is he making here? Which elements would you say he is most ignoring? (A: Affection.) Why? (A: he's cold, aloof, distant, stand-offish.) (A: Acknowledgment.) Why? (A: he invalidates her experience.) (But he's also not paying attention to how she's responding, or accepting the fact that she is seriously ill.)
17:56	Social services administrator talks about agendas	*"Take the cues from the patient. Don't come in with an agenda."* An agenda is the single biggest obstacle to paying attention. It includes: rehearsing what you're going to say; being focused entirely on what you're going to do for the person; or getting caught up in your own feelings, needs and opinions.
18:15	Karen talks about giving choices.	*"You want to give control... to give choice to the person you're visiting...no one (else) is asking permission to walk in... but if you do... you've empowered the person you're with."* Why is this important? What happens if you don't?

TIME ON VIDEO	SCENE	COMMENTS/LEARNING POINTS
18:50	Social service administrator talks about the greatest gift you can give someone.	*"One of the greatest gifts you can give to an individual who is ill, is to be present for them, and to continue to honor and respect them, helping them to see that they've made a difference."*
19:25	Interlude: Karen's story about meeting lepers in Ethiopia.	*"I remember at age seven, living in Addis Ababa, Ethiopia… three lepers standing on the outside of the marketplace… the forgotten ones…three white sheets… wrapped up all of his sores… he looked right into my eyes, here was a tear… Who stole the sheets?… I made a promise… I will never shut down my heart."*
23:20	**AFFECTION** definition	*The human touch of warmth, comfort, humor and kindness.* (Note: in the background is a *heart* monitor!)
23:30	Nurse talks about affection	*"It takes no extra time to hold a hand… to look a person in the eye. It's more than verbal communication…"*
23:48	Affection montage	Song.
24:25	Karen talks about being appropriate in the way you show affection.	*"Some people are very reserved… and are comfortable with a handshake… some of us like to hug, but not everybody likes to hug."*
25:10	Doctor tells a story about a Hopi Indian and water.	*"The Hopi Indian was doing his chants on the edge of a barren desert mesa and every song was about water… the anthropologist said, don't you sing about anything other than water? …water is very important to us here, there isn't very much of it… in American music almost every song is about love. Is that because you don't have very much of it?"*
25:56	Volunteer visit Karen comments (off camera)	*"Your willingness just to be there with them… you're not afraid of their illness… You are seeing what is right with this person, not what's wrong.*
26:17	High school volunteer shares what it's like to really connect with someone.	*"It's this contact between two people…I really touched somebody's life today, and maybe vice versa that somebody touched mine."*

TIME ON VIDEO	SCENE	COMMENTS/LEARNING POINTS
26:38	**ACCEPTANCE** definition	*Allowing things to be the way they are.*
26:48	Young man (Scott) visits male stroke patient (Gene)	*"What kind of business were you in?" "I set up bakeries."*
27:17	Karen comments about the interaction.	*"People don't like to be seen as patients. They like to be seen as people."*
27:38	Gene talking to Scott.	*"All my life I feared a stroke…I know how disastrous they can be… the people are very compassionate here."*
28:09	Karen comments	*"…watch how he's dropping deeper into his feelings…"*
28:27	Gene talks to Scott	*"I'm a very emotional guy, don't get me started…I've got a lot of problems… the nurses are so busy…but they had compassion…"* *(He starts to cry.)*
29:04	Karen comments	*"…Scott listens to him cry, then he reaches over and touches him…and says O.K.…he's not doing it in a condescending way… he didn't invalidate his feelings… He (Scott) has paid attention to the man, he's acknowledged him, he knows what kind of affection this man will receive… and accepts him for him, not focused on his disease, but focused on him as a man – and is genuinely delivering compassion."*
30:32	Priest talking, on a bench in a field.	*"The more you can respect and honor a person where they are at, the more doors you open for them… it's the ability to be with somebody, and not be afraid of their anger or sadness… if we can't handle our own, it's going to be difficult to handle someone else's."*
31:31	Young male volunteer (Scott) - interview	*Sometimes a sickness or a stroke is a turning point…and from there can come growth…to see that transition is a privilege"*
32:01	Nursing Director interview	*"Visitors connect on a very personal basis…they're not there to achieve an outcome… just to be whatever the patient or family needs… it's an important role… people feel cared about."*

TIME ON VIDEO	SCENE	COMMENTS/LEARNING POINTS
32:50	Karen visiting bald young man (Richard) with cancer.	*"I treat my volunteer work as sacred…the whole key is to be in the moment."*
33:05	Young man (Richard) talking	*"…my mom is sitting by the bed, she wants to go eat lunch. I told her no don't go … because I'm going to go whenever you leave… she didn't understand. I told her I'm going home… I had to, I was in too much pain."* (Crying) What is Richard really talking about? (A: his death.)
33:53	Nurse interview	*"… we think we have to have the answers… a lot of us don't know the answers, and we shouldn't pretend that we know the answers."* This is one of the biggest blocks to acceptance: pretending to know the answers. Be willing to say, "I don't know."
34:03	Karen's story about her first visit (black & white scene)	*"The first day that I went into the hospital, I was quite nervous… I was walking into the unknown…a couple of sisters asked me to visit their brother… he hasn't been able to speak for eight months… he said everything with his eyes… I told his sisters good-bye, and as I walked out the door, I heard 'I love you' – and this was the man."* Notice that even though Karen has a wealth of experience now, she was nervous the first time she volunteered at the hospital.
35:41	Karen's closing remarks., from the garden.	*"So from that moment on… when people would ask me… I would say, 'Come with me… get to know the wisdom of the elders. Get to know the wisdom of someone who may only have a month to live. Let them share with you what life's about.' … you will then have a greater compassion for mankind. It's impossible not to."*
36:52	Closing song and credits	
39:56	End of song and credits	

THE FOUR ELEMENTS[4]: DEFINITIONS, KEY WORDS AND OBSTACLES

The Four Elements are the ingredients that make communication meaningful, uplifting and satisfying. They are also four basic human needs. Everyone, and especially those who face adversity, deeply need and want your attention, acknowledgment, affection, and acceptance. When you deliver these, your efforts to give assistance are all the more appreciated.

By applying the Four Elements you will continue to improve your skills as a communicator, continue to deepen your insight into life, and continue to experience the true beauty and satisfaction of putting compassion into action.

Attention

at•ten•tion

Being aware of the signs, signals and clues that indicate what is important to someone.
— Adventures in Caring definition

Careful observing or listening; observant consideration or courtesy.
— American Heritage Dictionary definition

ASPECTS OF ATTENTION

➤ Listening. Seeing. Feeling.
➤ Asking permission (to enter, visit, help, support).
➤ Giving choices, giving control; e.g. "Is this a good time for me to visit?"
➤ Accepting his answer, whether yes or no.
➤ Observing the subtleties in a person's body language, tone of voice, facial expressions.
➤ Responding to her signals; following her lead.
➤ Going with what he wants to talk about, or discuss.
➤ Recognizing what is appreciated, and what isn't.
➤ Focusing on what is right with a person, rather than what's wrong.

---

4 These descriptions of the Four Elements are also included as handouts, in the pocket inside the back cover.

OBSTACLES TO PAYING ATTENTION
Following your own agenda instead of her lead.
➤ Not asking permission.
➤ Not giving any choices, or a sense of control.
➤ Intruding, interrupting, controlling.
➤ Getting caught up in your own feelings, opinions and needs.
➤ Focusing only on what you are **doing to** her, or **doing for** her, but avoiding **being with** her.

Making Assumptions
➤ Assuming the worst. Assuming the best.
➤ Assuming he wants your help, or your company.
➤ Never asking questions to check that you understood.
➤ Ignoring the signals, being insensitive.
➤ Ignoring signs on the door.
➤ Never noticing how someone is feeling.

Acknowledgment

ac•knowl•edg•ment

Letting someone know that you recognize and appreciate him as a unique individual.
– ADVENTURES IN CARING definition

Recognition of someone's existence or validity.
An expression of appreciation.
– AMERICAN HERITAGE DICTIONARY definition

ASPECTS OF ACKNOWLEDGMENT
➤ Appreciation. Respect.
➤ Taking a genuine interest in the person.
➤ Asking good questions.
➤ Talking about what's special, important or interesting to him.
➤ Helping people feel needed, wanted and valued.
➤ Commenting on how she has made a difference.
➤ Recognizing abilities, qualities and strengths.
➤ Validation, affirmation.

OBSTACLES TO ACKNOWLEDGMENT

Giving advice:
➤ "What you really need to do is think positive."
➤ "Make sure you take your vitamins." "You ought to get more exercise."
➤ "I read this great book that says you should drink more water."

Invalidating/discounting/denying someone's feelings, perspective or experience:
➤ "I know you don't really feel that way." "Don't cry!" "Don't worry. It's not as bad as you think."
➤ Being patronizing: "There, there, it'll be all right."
➤ Using cliches: "It could have been worse." "Every cloud has a silver lining."

One-upmanship:
➤ "You think your stitches are bad, you should see the scar from my gallbladder operation." "This is nothing, you should've seen Fred when it happened to him."
➤ Telling your tale of woe: "When I gave birth to you I was in labor for 48 hours – you've never felt such pain."
➤ Telling horror stories: (about surgical mistakes, incompetent doctors, malpractice lawsuits). "I heard that one of your doctor's patients just died."

af•fec•tion

The human touch of warmth, comfort, humor and kindness.
— ADVENTURES IN CARING definition

A fond or tender feeling toward another.
— AMERICAN HERITAGE DICTIONARY definition

ASPECTS OF AFFECTION
➤ Finding common ground.
➤ Sharing.
➤ Being together.

> Warmth. Comfort. Kindness.
> Thoughtful. Considerate.
> Appropriate use of touch.
> Heart. Joy. Good humor.
> Smiles.

OBSTACLES TO AFFECTION

Separating yourself:
> Showing no warmth, no feelings, no empathy.
> Being distant and aloof.
> Taking yourself too seriously.
> Finding no common ground.
> Staring, or its opposite, no eye contact.
> Talking about her as if she were an object, a body, or as if she were not in the same room.
> Talking down to someone, being condescending.

Feeling sorry:
> Commiserating: "Poor dear, I feel so sorry for you." "It must be awful."

Acceptance

ac•cep•tance

Allowing things to be the way they are.
– Adventures in Caring definition

Favorable reception. The act of receiving, esp. gladly.
To regard as usual. To bear patiently.
– American Heritage Dictionary definition

ASPECTS OF ACCEPTANCE

> Helping people feel safe and comfortable with you.
> Non-judgmental.
> No pretenses.
> Humility. Being willing to say, "I don't know."
> Faith.
> Open. Non-grasping. Open to change.
> Letting go of wanting it to be a certain way.
> Letting it be all right, as it is.
> Giving her permission to speak freely.
> Giving him permission to express his feelings.
> Universal Love. Agape.

OBSTACLES TO ACCEPTANCE

Avoiding & Pretending:
➤ Pretending that the situation is different from the way it really is.
➤ Pretending to know the answer when you don't.
➤ Avoiding the difficult issues that people may want to talk about.
➤ Avoiding the obvious or the inevitable.

Rescuing/Fixing it:
➤ Trying to rescue people from their problems.
➤ Trying to fix it, change it, or make it all better; but not helping him cope with the present situation.

Negativity:
➤ Getting irritated, complaining, blaming, finding fault.
➤ Being critical, judgmental, sarcastic, cynical, bitter.
➤ Being indifferent, blasé … whatever.
➤ Getting defensive, taking it personally, being inflexible.
➤ Laying guilt: "If only you hadn't smoked all these years, this never would have happened." "Think of all the worry you've caused Mom." "I read that you're responsible for your own illnesses."

WHAT CAN I SAY[5] (an excerpt)

"Susan has been crying for two days straight," said the charge nurse. "I'm concerned that the depression is interfering with her recovery – and there's nothing more we can do for her medically. Would you go in and visit with her? Maybe you can lift her spirits." I took a deep breath and accepted the challenge.

Before entering the patient's room I knocked gently on her door. "Is it O.K. if I come and visit with you for a few minutes?" I asked. Between the sobbing I heard a faint "O.K." Knowing the situation was sensitive I made a special effort to pay attention.

Susan was doubled up in a fetal position, crying into her pillow, kleenex boxes strewn around the bed. By her body

5 Excerpt from the book, "What Can I Say? A Guide to Visiting Friends and Family Who Are Ill", by Karen and Simon Fox.

55

language and the tension in her voice, I could tell that she was not just depressed, but very frightened.

"Sometimes I find it hard to feel brave" I said. "Sometimes I feel like tears are the only answer." After a pause, I asked, "Would you like me to sit here with you?" Then, following my intuition, "Would you like me to hold you while you cry?"

Susan reached out her thin pale arms and fell into my embrace. I held her until the tears stopped.

I learned that Susan was a single mother, with no family and no income. She was worried about being too ill to look after her baby, and that he would end up in a foster home. She was so afraid of not getting well she was making herself sick.

As we talked, her confidence grew. I gave her control of the conversation, and a chance to talk freely about what was on her mind, without fear of judgment. We held hands and shed a few tears.

A few days later Susan met me at the hospital elevator, I.V. pole in hand. "Your visit made all the difference. Now I think I can cope," she said, beaming. "I just needed to know that somebody cared. Thank you for making me feel wanted."

The charge nurse who was with her smiled at me and said, "When we've tried everything medically, it's amazing what a good listener and a little TLC can do."

⌒

There is no such thing as the "proper thing" to say when you visit someone who is ill. But there are four things you can do.

Almost everyone is starving for four basic human needs, and people who are ill need them the most. If you meet these needs your visit will be a blessing for you and the patient.

Everyone needs:

attention	acknowledgment
affection	acceptance

"The greatest challenge of the day is: how to bring about a revolution of the heart, a revolution which has to start with each one of us?"

— DOROTHY DAY

1. ATTENTION

People need you to pay attention to them. They need you to notice the little things. They need you to listen.

You can pay attention with your eyes, ears, nose, mind, and heart. Visitors often pay attention to what's wrong with the patient. That's the doctor's job. Your job is to focus on what's right with the patient, and help him remember what he's got going for him.

You can pay attention to a person's courage and their spirit, their memories and mannerisms. Each of us has a unique background, spiritual outlook, and state of mind. The key is to become genuinely interested in people as individuals, not as patients.

Whether you have just met or you have been together for a lifetime, don't assume you know everything about one another. Illness brings up new issues and new perspectives. If you look for the good, the beauty, the strength, the wisdom – you will find it.

An illness can be a tragedy – and a turning point. It is an opportunity for souls to meet. A chance for you to get to know one another in a much deeper way.

2. ACKNOWLEDGMENT

When you notice what is special about a person, you can comment on it. This is acknowledgment. With Susan I acknowledged her tears. I let her know that I noticed her sadness.

This is a fundamental need; to know that others recognize our existence. And even better, to know that others notice our individuality. You fulfill this need when you pay a compliment, appreciate uniqueness, or remind someone just how special they are.

You acknowledge people through your body language. A smile, moving closer, making eye contact, shows that you are interested. A twinkle in the eye, or a tear – a glance that says you care.

"The manner of giving is worth more than the gift."

– Pierre Corneille

Acknowledgment validates a person's experience – and one of the most powerful forms of acknowledgment is listening. Not just hearing, but asking the questions that draw out the best in people.

3. AFFECTION

Affection brings the human touch of warmth and caring into medicine. Kind and gentle touch is the cornerstone of a good visit.

Especially in the high-tech world of a modern hospital, patients are hungry for affection. Often, the most effective way to express kindness is through touch: holding hands, giving a hug, a kiss, or holding someone in your arms.

Each of these physical gestures can say "I love you," "I care about you." So can foot rubs, hand rubs or a shoulder massage to relieve tension. People who are seriously ill don't need you to be an expert – they need your love.

What you may understand to be affectionate may not be taken that way by everyone. People from different cultures and backgrounds, and people in pain, respond to affection in different ways. Make sure you notice what kind of affection suits them best. Remember that elderly patients are often fragile and their skin can bruise easily – so be gentle, be warm.

Show your affection in a way that you know will be appreciated. A smile is something that everyone understands. Hugs, waves, holding hands all add an essential warmth. Allow yourself to be personal – a close friend – warm and spontaneous. Most of all: follow your heart.

4. ACCEPTANCE

Acceptance means being non-judgmental, tolerant and forgiving. It means receiving the person just as they are.

Just holding Susan in my arms and letting her cry showed affection and acceptance. One gesture communicated tenderness and assurance.

Acceptance is not resignation or indifference. Acceptance means you have come to terms with the fact that what is – is. When people are sick, they need, more than ever, to know that you care. They need you to notice, to recognize, to share in their suffering.

Acceptance provides a safe zone in which people can talk freely about their hopes and fears, without the fear of being judged. Acceptance frees people to share their true feelings, to talk about difficult issues. It gives them a chance to talk honestly and openly – a rare opportunity for most of us.

TIPS FOR GROUP LEADERS

5

5

DO'S & DON'TS FOR GROUP LEADERS[6]

DO
Practice what you preach.
Apply the Four Elements to the way you lead the session, by:
➤ Paying attention to your audience – taking an interest in what they have to say; listening carefully to their responses.
➤ Acknowledging your audience – writing their responses on a flip chart and posting them on the wall; repeating back their answers to check that you understood.
➤ Showing affection – being warm and friendly; treating them as adults and as equals; joining with them in the process of learning.
➤ Accepting the different ways in which people learn, discover, remember, and express themselves.

DO
Introduce yourself and the video.
Prepare your audience by:
➤ Welcoming everyone to the session.
➤ Explaining your role as facilitator.
➤ Presenting the timeline for the session.
➤ Telling why you want them to see this video.
➤ Reviewing the possible benefits to the group.
➤ Disclosing how the video has been useful to you, and why you like it.
➤ Telling a story that leads to the video.

DO
Give instructions by:
➤ Letting them know why you are doing the exercise.

---

6 By Jill Morris, Management Training Company

➤ Building the exercise one step at a time.
➤ Keeping it simple.
➤ Checking that they understand what to do.

DON'T

➤ Discount or diminish what any participant says by saying "yes, but" or "no, but"; or by making facial expressions or gestures that indicate the speaker is not "doing it right."

DO

Validate each participants contribution by:
➤ Summarizing what you heard them say.
➤ Checking that you heard what they mean.
➤ Tying what they said to the current discussion, or asking them to do so.
➤ Using self-disclosure, by telling a story or making a comment about yourself that is related to what they have said, and to the content of the discussion.
➤ Asking clarifying questions to more fully understand what they mean.

DON'T

➤ Preach by telling people what they "should" do.
➤ Talk down to your audience by using a lot of sentences with "you" – implying that you know more about what they want, or should want, than they do.

DO

➤ Ask what they want.
➤ Ask what they know.
➤ Ask what would be useful or work for them.
➤ Ask if they want your advice or suggestions before giving any.

DON'T

➤ Assume that because people have seen the same video, they have the same interpretation of the content and message.

DO

> Remember each person is different, and has a different frame of reference – people have different interpretations, likes and dislikes, that differ from your own, and from the other members of the group.
> Avoid driving your interpretation as the "right" one.
> Find ways to communicate what can be useful and learned from each interpretation.

DO

> Remember your audience and pay attention to each person's needs and perspective. Each person has a different background: geography, age, gender, occupation, family, ethnicity, education, religion, and life experiences. All of this has shaped who they are and how they see the world. Whenever they speak, they will be sharing part of this with you.
> Listen for what you can learn about each participant.

DO

Prepare in advance for your audience:
> Learn about your participants in advance.
> Think about what comments and questions might arise in the session.
> Outline some ways you could respond.

DO

Plan how you will close the session:
> Share what you got out of it.
> Review the key points.
> Review what was gained.
> Ask others to share what they learned, what was most useful to them.
> Acknowledge them for participating.
> Outline next step for you, the participants, your program and/or your organization.

"Life is amazing: and the teacher had better prepare himself to be a medium for that amazement."

– Edward Blishen

LISTENING SKILLS THAT BUILD PARTICIPATION[7]

If your group is known to be particularly quiet or reserved; or if there is a general lack of involvement in the discussions, here are some skills that encourage participation.

It is vitally important for the facilitator to listen carefully to *everyone,* not just a favored few. Some people find it hard to get their ideas across in meetings, because they don't communicate in acceptable ways. They may be shy or nervous; they may speak slowly or in broken sentences. Others may be repetitious, domineering or exaggerate the facts. And some may be impulsive or very emotional.

A facilitator who listens well can help *everyone* participate. Even though a thought may not be presented with great style, a facilitator can help people convey the substance of their ideas to the group, by using the following listening skills.

- **Encouraging:** creates an opening for people to participate, without putting anyone on the spot. Statements like: "Who else has an idea?" "Let's hear from someone who hasn't spoken in a while" give everyone permission to join in. Comments like, "Can anyone give us another example of this" can help people discover an aspect of the topic that engages them.

- **Balancing:** "Does anyone have a different idea?" "Are there other ways of looking at this." The direction of a discussion often follows the lead of the people who speak first. Balancing rounds out the discussion and gives permission for other views to be expressed. (This is not for the purpose of argument or debate, but as a means of collecting a variety of perspectives.)

- **Making Space:** Watch for quiet members of the group, and when the timing seems right, gently invite them to speak. "Was there a thought you wanted to express?" "Did you want to add anything?" If they decline, be gracious. Don't pressure

"When love and skill work together, expect a master-piece."

– John Ruskin

7 Adapted from the book "Facilitator's Guide to Participatory Decision-Making" by Sam Kaner. For more instruction on making meetings work, contact Community at Work at (415)641-9773

anyone to speak; no one likes to be put on the spot. If participation is very uneven, suggest a structured go-around to give anyone who wants to, a chance to speak.

- **Using the Clock:** "We only have time for one or two more comments. Perhaps we could hear from someone who hasn't had a chance to speak yet. Who wants to speak?" This statement raises the stakes a little: if you want to speak, now's your chance.

- **Paraphrasing:** is using your own words to say what you think the speaker said. Begin your paraphrase with a comment like, "It sounds like what you're saying is… " "Am I hearing you correctly, is this what you mean… ?" Look for the speaker's reaction, and end the paraphrase with something like, "Is that correct?" If not, keep asking for clarification until the speaker feels understood.

- **Drawing People Out:** is particularly useful when someone is having difficulty clarifying an idea, or articulating a feeling. After paraphrasing her statement, follow up with an open-ended question such as, "Can you say more about that?" or "What do you mean by that?" or "Can you be more specific?"

N O T E : Paraphrasing and drawing people out, should be used sparingly. When used too much they can be tiresome. Use them only as a way to help speakers who are clearly having difficulty expressing themselves.

ADULT LEARNING PRINCIPLES

The *Communicating with Compassion* discussion and workshop is designed using adult learning principles. Therefore it is suitable for people who can relate to being treated as adults – generally speaking, those who are sixteen years and older.

Please bear in mind the following information as you prepare to lead the discussion or workshop. Applying these principles will go a long way toward ensuring the success of your program.

Use the following checklist of the eight adult learning principles to evaluate if you are applying them to your learning session:

DOES THE LEARNING SESSION[8]:

➤ Focus on "real world" problems?

➤ Emphasize how participants can apply what happens in the group?

➤ Relate the group activities to the goals of the participants?

➤ Relate the materials to their past experiences?

➤ Allow debate and challenge of ideas?

➤ Listen to and respect the opinions of group members?

➤ Encourage members to share resources?

➤ Treat everyone in an adult-like manner?

Adult learning principles are important to learn and use as a trainer or facilitator. If you use adult learning principles, both to develop workshop designs and to facilitate your groups, you'll increase the likelihood that your adult group members will learn, be committed to their goals, and generate more solutions to problems.

8 From the book, "Training Methods That Work", by Lois B. Hart. Reprinted with permission. Crisp Publications Inc., 1200 Hamilton Court, Menlo Park, CA 94025; (800) 442-7477 or (415) 323-6100.

DIFFERENCES BETWEEN CHILDREN AND ADULTS AS LEARNERS

CHILDREN	ADULT
Rely on others to decide what is important to be learned.	Decide for themselves what is important to be learned.
Accept the information being presented at face value.	Need to validate the information based on their beliefs and experiences.
Expect that what they are learning will be useful in their long-term future.	Expect that what they are learning is immediately useful.
Have little or no experience upon which to draw – are relatively "clean slates".	Have much past experience upon which to draw – may have fixed viewpoints.
Have little ability to serve as a knowledgeable resource to teacher or fellow classmates.	Have significant ability to serve as a knowledgeable resource to the facilitator and group members.
Are content centered.	Are problem centered.
Are less actively involved.	Actively participate.
Learn in an authority-oriented environment.	Function best in a collaborative environment.
Planning is teacher's responsibility.	Share in planning.

LEADING A FOCUSED DISCUSSION[9]

SITUATION	WHAT TO DO	EXAMPLES
1. Getting Started	Assure a pleasant climate with no interruptions before the session begins. Uncluttered, tidy space.	*"Let's get started. Joanne, will you please close the door?"*
	Provide a context as the session begins: "what we are doing is important."	*"What we'll do in this session is take a look at how to put compassion into practice. We'll explore four keys to creating rapport with the people you help . We'll also examine what gets in the way of good communication."*
	The first question should be asked with precision. Have it written down before you start.	
	Go around the room and ask each person to answer the first one or two questions so that everyone's voice is heard early in the conversation.	*"What moment or scene from the video stands out for you? John, why don't we start with you and go around the room to your left."*
2. Keeping track of ideas	Write brief phrases on your own note pad after each response.	*"You mentioned these scenes." (Read back the list.) "Which of these shows an example of good listening?*
	Ask someone to write key words from the group's responses on a flip chart.	
	Use the notes to recap between questions.	
3. Keeping the discussion going	If nobody answers, repeat the question; reword or rephrase as a last resort.	*"O.K., someone else, what was the first of the Four Elements described in the video?"*
	If participants get off the topic, repeat the question.	
	If someone grandstands or talks a long time, ask for a specific example; ask if someone else has a specific example.	

9 Adapted from the book, "Group Facilitation Methods", by the Institute of Cultural Affairs. Reprinted with permission.

SITUATION	WHAT TO DO	EXAMPLES
4. Maintaining focus	When the group begins to stray off the subject, recap briefly what has been said so far. Acknowledge and "bracket" the distraction Repeat the question.	*"That is an important concern. Let's bring it up next time we do our work schedule. Now, will someone share with us how you think the Four Elements could affect patient satisfaction?"*
5. Keeping the discussion practical	When you introduce the question, give a practical example yourself.	*"Yesterday I heard a volunteer ask a patient if she lived nearby. What are some other good questions you could ask to open up a conversation?"*
6. Resolving Disagreements	You don't have to. It's helpful to have many points of view in the discussion. If people argue, don't take sides, but ask the group if there are other viewpoints. If someone disagrees, have them say what their own idea is, rather than just disagree. Review what was discussed.	*"Strong feelings are O.K., but we have to get a wide range of ideas, too."* *"It looks like we have at least three perspectives here. Are there any others?"*.
7. Bringing the Discussion to a Close	If you made notes, use them to help you recap the discussion. Let the group know of any next steps that may result from the discussion. Acknowledge everyone's participation	*"We have covered a lot of ground today.... "*

TIMEKEEPING AND CHARTWRITING

Having one or two assistants to help you conduct the workshop makes life a little easier, and it makes the workshop more efficient and effective. Ask your group for one or two volunteers to help you with timekeeping and/or chartwriting.

The timekeeper's duties are to watch the time, and remind you when time is almost up for a particular section of the workshop (see the session timelines in chapters 2 and 3 for timing details). This frees you to focus on what the participants are saying, rather than watching the clock. Staying on schedule is important; but it is not more important than a fruitful discussion.

The chartwriter's duties are to record the responses of the group on a flip chart and hang the pages on the wall. This serves as the "group memory," a visual record reminding the class of the material they've covered. It also acknowledges each person's contribution to the discussion: people can see that they were heard, and this encourages participation.

EVALUATION

At the end of the session you might want to ask the audience for some feedback. Let them know that their input is important, because it will help you plan future sessions.

This information will help you gauge what the audience learned from the session, what they found useful, how well they liked it, and it gives clues on how the session might be improved upon in the future. A sample evaluation form is included in the handouts folder.

To evaluate, consider whether you achieved your objectives. Compare the feedback you got with the objectives of the session. Then make the necessary adjustments to improve the next session. For example, you may want to adjust the timing of the session, or re-work some of the questions to make them a better fit for the needs of your group.

The key to success in presenting these sessions is not doing it perfectly the first time, but in each session finding a way to

Who is wise?

He who learns

from all men.

– TALMUD, SAYINGS
  OF THE FATHERS

improve upon what you did before. Feedback from your audience will give you clues on how to do this.

SELF-DISCOVERY AND EXPERIENCE-BASED LEARNING

By far the most powerful way for anyone to learn, is through self-discovery. More than being told what to do, people remember best the things they discover for themselves. This is why a well-guided discussion is so powerful; because a lot of discovery can take place within a discussion.

Unlike teaching by lecturing, learning through discussion takes advantage of the collective wisdom of the group. With adult education, this is a key resource. Your group members will learn from each other. Even with young men and women, their diverse perspectives and life experiences provide a rich source of knowledge, which is well-suited to the goal of learning more about how to communicate with compassion.

Your audience will learn even more about *Communicating with Compassion* by actually interacting with someone who is ill, injured, alone or in distress. With a longer session, you might consider taking an hour out to visit the nearest nursing home, a senior center, people who are shut-in at home, or a homeless shelter etc. In this way the participants gain some first-hand experience. When you return to the classroom, the discussion will be richer and more realistic.

If time doesn't permit a visit during the session, suggest that participants visit someone in need, between this session and the next. Remind them to put the Four Elements into action, and to notice what happens. In the follow-up session discuss their experiences.

"The supreme happiness of life is the conviction that we are loved; loved for ourselves."

– Victor Hugo

CLOSING THE SESSION

Always close on an up note. Near the end of the session, if someone brings up a depressing experience or a difficult issue, make sure you get the group back on track before closing.

It is essential to end the session with everyone feeling good about their experience. If necessary, you can re-focus things with a final question, such as, "What did you enjoy most about the session today?" A few replies will quickly alter the mood of the group and leave people feeling positive about their experience.

As you close the session encourage the participants to really connect with people in need – to take an interest in the lives of these people, and put the Four Elements into action. Remind your audience how much people need their personal attention, acknowledgment, affection and acceptance.

The more you remember to add these Four Elements to your interactions, the more skilled a communicator you become, and the more your assistance will be appreciated. It can make all the difference in the world.

CLASS EXERCISES

- What Went Wrong?

- What Went Right?

- Asking Permission
  Demonstration

6

CLASS EXERCISES

6

The exercises described below are additional ways to help your group gain a deeper understanding of the subject. They can be added to the three-hour workshop format to make it a more comprehensive session.

WHAT WENT WRONG?

 EXERCISE PURPOSE:
➤ to recognize the errors that make compassionate communication impossible.

Give out to the class the handouts on the Four Elements. Have them read the obstacles to the Four Elements. Now have the class watch the "blooper" scenes from the video, one at a time. (See Time Index in chapter 4 for where they are located on the video.)

After each "blooper" stop the tape and ask the class, "What did he (or she) do wrong here? As people call out the answers, write them up on the flip chart. Here are some (but not all) of the answers:

What did the young woman do wrong? (scene starts at 16:22)
➤ Got caught up in her own feelings: nervous.
➤ Never asked a question.
➤ Never gave a choice.
➤ Controlled the conversation.
➤ Assumed the best.
➤ Never noticed how the patient was feeling.
➤ Spoke much too quickly for a patient who looked like she was sedated, and much too chirpy for someone in pain.
➤ Gave advice: "Make sure you get those tests done."

> ➤ Invalidated: "You shouldn't be worried."
> "We're doing fine without you."
> "It'll be a piece of cake."
> ➤ Very little eye contact.
> ➤ Found no common ground.
> ➤ Pretended to know the answers: "You'll be back at work soon."
> ➤ Avoided any depth of feeling.

What did the older couple do wrong? (scene starts at 16:49)
Lack of attention:
> ➤ Never noticed how she was feeling.
> ➤ Caught up in his own speculation and worries.
> ➤ Asked no questions.
> ➤ Gave no choices.
> ➤ Made no eye contact.
> ➤ Talked as if the patient wasn't even in the room.
> ➤ Impersonal, indifferent attitude toward her future.
> ➤ Told horror stories : "worst case they ever had" "maybe they lied."

What did the young man do wrong? (scene starts at 17:10)
> ➤ Standing over the patient.
> ➤ Staring at the patient.
> ➤ Stand-offish, aloof, (standing at the end of the bed, arms folded).
> ➤ Invalidated: "No big deal," "It's not so bad."
> ➤ Indifferent to her condition.
> ➤ Assumed she felt O.K.
> ➤ Assumed she wanted his company.
> ➤ Ignored her body language.

Conclude the exercise by pointing out that: **all of these mistakes are due to the absence of one or more of the Four Elements.**

 Here is a key that gives each member of your group a way to continue building good communication skills – for life. By using the Four Elements as a guide one can quickly diagnose a communications problem.

If you are having difficulty developing rapport with someone you're trying to help; if you don't seem to get along; if you

"When you are introduced to someone, of course you want to make a good impression. The trouble arises because that someone wants to make a good impression on you too; and both of you are so busy making a good impression on one another that neither of you has really met the other at all."

– ANN DAVIES

misunderstand one another; take a step back and ask yourself, "Which element is missing here? Attention, Acknowledgment, Affection or Acceptance?"

WHAT WENT RIGHT?

 EXERCISE PURPOSE:
➤ to recognize the Four Elements in action, and understand how they add up to a satisfying and meaningful interaction.

Conduct this exercise, in a similar manner to the previous one, but now focus on what the visitors were doing right. The visits that go well seem so natural and easy, and we rarely notice why the visit went so well. Here is a chance for your group to discover what these people did to create such good rapport.

What did the high school volunteer do right? (starts at 6:45)
➤ Took nothing for granted.
➤ She asked permission to enter.
➤ Asked good questions, took an interest in his life.
➤ Didn't take herself seriously/good sense of humor/ willing to laugh when appropriate.
➤ Willing to be serious when appropriate.
➤ Followed the patient's lead.
➤ Accepted that he couldn't speak clearly, and didn't finish his sentences for him.
➤ Good eye contact.
➤ Physically on his level; made it easy for him to look at her.
➤ Spoke slowly so he could understand.
➤ Repeated back statements to make sure she understood.
➤ Appropriate use of affection; holding hands.
➤ Perceptive acknowledgment about his attitude.

What did the young man (who visits the man with a stroke) do right? (scene starts at 26:48)
➤ Asked good questions: took an interest in his life and work.
➤ Good eye contact.

➤ Found common ground.
➤ Listened without interrupting.
➤ Let him to talk about what was important to him.
➤ Allowed him to express his feelings.
➤ Appropriate use of affection.
➤ Accepted how he felt/what he was struggling with.
➤ Acknowledged his family (earlier in the video).

ASKING PERMISSION DEMONSTRATION

 EXERCISE PURPOSE:
➤ to demonstrate how asking permission changes the comfort level of the person you visit.

First the leader explains the concept of personal space. Stand up and put your arms and fingers straight out (horizontally). Explain that from tip of the finger to the surface of the body, all the way around us, is regarded by most people as our comfort zone or personal space. Demonstrate this by holding your arms out and turning in a circle, to show the circumference of the comfort zone.

Tell your audience, "Imagine that you are a king or queen, and this comfort zone is your castle. Most castles have a moat around them, to distance them from danger. And these castles have a drawbridge. The drawbridge is closed when you want no one to enter your castle, or personal space. When someone asks permission to enter, you have a choice to let him in or not. If you choose to let him in, you let the drawbridge down, and he can enter. If he doesn't ask permission, you remain closed, and any approach is regarded as an intrusion. (And the person is perceived, subconsciously, as an adversary. He may also fall in the moat!)"

Now ask four to six people to help you demonstrate. Have them stand in a semicircle in front of you. The rest of the group observes.

You (the leader) chooses at random one of the people standing in the semicircle, and walks up to her. The leader

"To him a man was always a man, an individual who did not disappear in a crowd."

– G.K. CHESTERTON ON ST. FRANCIS OF ASSISI

approaches slowly, face-to-face, but never asks permission or says anything.

The leader gets closer and closer and closer, until you are within about six inches of the person. Stand there until she reacts (unless she has already reacted.)

The leader then moves back and asks the people who are participating in the demonstration, "What did you notice?" If time permits, get more comments by asking the rest of the class, "What did you observe?" Get several responses, especially about what her body language was saying. Then ask the person you intruded on, "How did that make you feel?" "What did you want to do?" Give her time to articulate her feelings to the class.

Now announce to everyone that you will repeat the exercise with just one difference.

Face the same person you approached before. Before walking up to her, this time you ask permission to come into her space. For example: "May I enter your space?" or, "Would you mind if I stood near you?" After asking the question, remain still and wait until she gives you permission. Only then do you approach as you did before; closer and closer, face-to-face. Again, allow her to react naturally.

Now ask the others (and the class if time permits) "What did you notice this time?" "What differences did you observe, compared to the first interaction?" Then ask the person you approached "How did you feel this time?" "What made the difference?"

After hearing several responses, go on to repeat the exercise with the others who are helping you demonstrate. Again, choose your next person at random (pick someone who is least expecting it.) First intrude on his personal space by walking up without asking permission. Ask for observations from the group, and then from him. Then repeat your approach, but ask permission first. Again, ask for observations, especially on the difference between the first approach and the second, in his body language and in his feelings.

Repeat the two kinds of approaches with each of your helpers, asking for observations after each approach. This not only reinforces the point about asking permission before visiting with or helping someone. It also gives the class some practice in observing the different kinds of body language that people use to say "I'm uncomfortable with you," or "I'm happy you're here."

Conclude by noting what a difference it makes when you simply ask permission, and respect the person's choice.

NOTE: This is not an exercise to show the appropriate use of affection; nor is it intended to be an example of asking good questions; but only to demonstrate the power of asking permission.

NOTE: If one of the people helping you does not give you permission to enter his space, be gracious and thank him, and then go on to someone else in the group.

APPENDIX

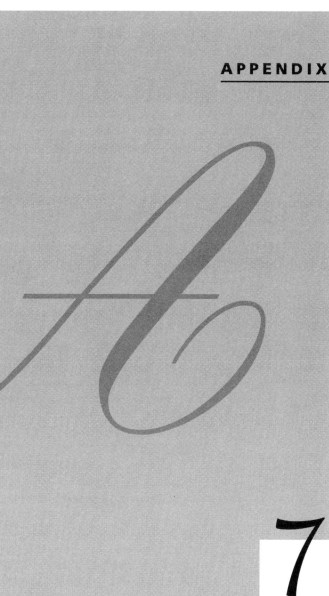

7

7

PHOTOCOPYING POLICY

To make it easier for group leaders to do their job, we are granting permission to the purchaser of *Communicating with Compassion* to photocopy the handouts included with this package. This gives you the freedom to make as many photocopies of the handouts as you need, without having to purchase more copies. In return we ask that you give credit to Adventures in Caring by not removing the copyright line at the bottom of each handout page.

Permission to photocopy means only that: permission to photocopy. It does not grant the right to reproduce the material in any other way, or include it in any other publication.

The permission to photocopy does **not** extend to making copies of this Leader Guide. For more copies of this publications please call the Adventures in Caring Foundation, toll-free, at 1-800-833-5678.

YOUR VIDEO LICENSE

Your license for the *Communicating with Compassion* video is written on the label of the videocassette. It reads as follows:

This videocassette is licensed for individual and internal organizational use only. All other uses, including any presentations to the public, are prohibited. No portion of the program contained in this videocassette may be reproduced, broadcast or re-transmitted in any manner or by any means, without prior written consent.

In other words, the video may be used in-house, for presentations to your members, staff, students and volunteers; and also for private home use. But you may not use the video for any presentations to the public. This includes not using the video in things such as: public seminars, speaking engagements, broadcasts, advertising, fundraising or special events.

It is illegal to copy any portion of the program contained in the video, in any way, for any reason. We appreciate you complying with your license. By doing so you help us to maintain the quality and integrity of the product.

THE DISCUSSION METHOD[10]

The primary tool for getting the most out of the video is a discussion method called the O.R.I.D. Discussion Method. This method is described in more detail below, but here is a brief overview.

The O.R.I.D. Discussion Method was designed by the Institute of Cultural Affairs, and is described in its books *Group Facilitation Methods* and *Winning Through Participation* (see bibliography.) We used the O.R.I.D. Discussion Method to come up with the questions for the ninety-minute and three-hour formats in chapters 2 and 3.

We chose this particular method because it is a natural and powerful way for a group to learn together. It doesn't require that the group leader be an expert, and it is an excellent way to help a group share its ideas and insights.

O.R.I.D. stands for the four stages of the discussion, and for the four types of questions that are used to guide the conversation.

Objective: the facts, observations: what is seen and heard.

Reflective: the feelings, emotions, associations and subjective observations: what is felt.

Interpretive: the meaning, insight, purpose, importance and relevant personal experience (not opinions or judgments): what is understood.

Decisional: the action to be taken, the choices, resolutions, responses, new behavior: what is to be done.

I don't know what your destiny will be, but one thing I know: the only ones among you who will be really happy are those who have sought and found how to serve.

— ALBERT SCHWEITZER

10 For further training in group facilitation methods, contact the Institute of Cultural Affairs at (800) 742-4032 or J.W. Ballard at (805) 969-9313.

In each discussion, our lists of suggested questions follow these four categories.

For best results each discussion should also have a definite purpose. This purpose is the destination toward which you, as the session facilitator, guide the group. For each discussion, along with a list of suggested questions to guide the discussion, we have also stated the purpose of the discussion indicated by a lighthouse icon.

O.R.I.D. DISCUSSION METHOD DETAILS[11]

The following details on the O.R.I.D. Discussion Method are included so that you can use it with a variety of subjects and settings, or adapt the *Communicating with Compassion* material to more specialized training needs.

For best results a discussion should always be tailored to the needs of the group. Since the questions that guide the discussion must be relevant to the topic and to the group, they should be prepared in advance, using the following three steps:

- *Step One: Rational Objective* Write down the rational objective. This is what you want the group to learn from the session. For example, one of the rational objectives of discussing this video is that participants will discover at least one way to improve the way they communicate.

- *Step Two: Experiential Objective* Write down the experiential objective. This is what you want the participants to feel as a result of the conversation. In this case, one of the experiential objectives is that participants will be motivated to put the Four Elements of *Communicating with Compassion* into practice.

- *Step Three: O.R.I.D. Questions* Write out the four levels of questions you will use to guide the discussion: objective, reflective, interpretive and decisional. Write several questions for each step of the discussion. Then review the whole discussion

11 For more information on working with groups, we recommend the books "Winning Through Participation" and "Group Facilitation Methods", listed in the bibliography.

and select the best one or two questions for each step. The best questions are the ones that will direct the discussion toward your rational and experiential objectives. More than ten questions can make for an unwieldy discussion.

Questions should be specific and open ended. They should not be answered with a simple "yes" or "no". Questions at the objective level should be easy to answer and inviting to help break the ice. As a general rule, there should be two to three questions at the objective level, two at the reflective and interpretive levels, and one or two at the decisional level. This rule is flexible, and with practice, you will learn what works best in different situations.

DISCUSSION METHOD OVERVIEW

OPENING
WELCOME
CONTEXT

RATIONAL OBJECTIVE
What does the team need to know, or to understand, or to decide?
What topic does the group need to develop?

EXPERIENTIAL OBJECTIVE
What does the team needs to experience with each other?
eg. excitement
intrigue with a new idea
authentic struggle

CLOSING
COMMENTS
REFLECTIONS

O BJECTIVE
‖‖‖

GETTING THE FACTS
Focus attention.

Questions begin with what people

-- see
-- hear
-- touch
-- smell
-- taste

R EFLECTIVE
‖‖‖ ↰

EMOTIONS, FEELINGS, ASSOCIATIONS
Questions illuminate:
--People's emotional responses

-- What they feel about something - what angers, excites, intrigues or frightens

-- What past associations they have

I NTERPRETIVE
‖‖‖ ↰↰

VALUES, MEANING, PURPOSE
Questions highlight:
-- Layers of meaning and purpose

-- The significance people attach to a subject

-- The story out of which they live

D ECISIONAL
‖‖‖ ↰↰↰

FUTURE RESOLVES
Questions allow individuals to decide their relationship and response to the topic and the discussion they have had together.

HOW TO GET INVOLVED: NATIONAL RESOURCE GUIDE

As a result of the *Communicating with Compassion* workshop, the members of your audience may be inspired to volunteer. If you don't already have a volunteer program, here is a list of national resources who can refer you to local organizations who need volunteers.

The *Communicating with Compassion* workshop is focused on service that involves personal contact with the people who are helped. Not all volunteer jobs do. So be sure to ask an organization if its volunteers have personal contact with the people they serve.

Allan Luks, in his book *The Healing Power of Doing Good,* offers the following advice:
"In choosing a type of volunteering that will maximize your good feelings and health, and keep you coming back, remember to find an activity that offers the following:
- ➤ Personal contact with the person you help (especially a stranger.)
- ➤ The opportunity for frequent helping, with a rough goal of two hours weekly.
- ➤ A task that you are already equipped to do, or will be trained to do.
- ➤ An opportunity that is especially relevant to your interests.

"An organization can provide invaluable support for the helper. While one-on-one helping can be practiced through-out the day, doing some volunteer work through an organization makes helping easier to sustain and more rewarding.

"Whatever field interests you, it's likely that you will find local community groups working in that field. Whether it is literacy, feeding and sheltering the homeless, care of the elderly or disadvantaged children, poverty, or education, look it up by key word in your phone book. Or try looking up the word volunteer. Under this listing you may find local agencies that are clearinghouses for volunteer services."

If this approach doesn't produce results, look through the following list of organizations:

"Make yourself

necessary to

someone."

– RALPH WALDO
   EMERSON

VOLUNTEER OPPORTUNITIES

Points of Light Foundation
800/59-LIGHT   (202) 223-9186
1736 H. Street N.W., Washington, DC 20006
National 800 number for finding out about a huge variety of volunteer opportunities anywhere in America.

The organizations listed below can refer you to one of their chapters or affiliated organizations nationwide:

American Association of Disabled Persons
5840 North Orange Blossom Trail, Suite 210
Orlando, FL 32810
(800) 642-8775   (407) 880-9ADA
Internet address: 74774.3247@compuserve.com
AADP is an organization dedicated to preserving and uplifting the levels of dignity, unity and civil rights of disabled Americans. Our activities include providing social contact for disabled persons, advocacy/legal clinics, publication of the AADP newsletter and a volunteer resource center.

American Association Of Retired Persons
601 E Street, N.W.
Washington, D.C. 20049
(202) 434-2277   (800) 424-3410
AARP is dedicated to helping middle-aged and older Americans (50+), both working and retired, achieve lives of independence, dignity and purpose. AARP operates more than 30,000 volunteer programs nationwide. Other activities of the organization include: advocacy, Volunteer Talent Bank, and publication of Modern Maturity magazine.

American Red Cross
National Headquarters
431 18th Street NW
Washington, D.C. 20006
(202) 639-3378
The Red Cross brings together trained volunteers and paid staff to help prevent, prepare for, and cope with emergencies. The ARC is chartered by the U.S. Congress to provide disaster relief at home and abroad. It collects, processes and distributes voluntarily donated blood and involves over 1.5 million volunteers. The best way to volunteer for the ARC is to call your local chapter or contact the American Red Cross for the chapter nearest you.

Association of Junior Leagues International
660 First Avenue
New York, NY 10016
(212) 683-1515
AJLI is the advisory and consulting organization for 285 Junior Leagues across the U.S., Canada, Mexico and Great Britain. The Association and member Leagues, comprised of women, are united in a common purpose to promote volunteerism; to develop the potential of the League members for voluntary participation in community affairs; and to demonstrate the effectiveness of trained volunteers. Call the New York office for your local chapter.

Best Buddies
100 S.E. 2nd Street, Suite 1990
Miami, FL 33131
(800) 892-8339
Best Buddies is a national organization that operates on college and university campuses where college students can apply and be selected to serve as a "buddy" to a young adult, who is mentally retarded. These friendships promote regular interaction with the buddies.

Big Brothers/Big Sisters of America
230 N. 13th Street
Philadelphia, PA 19107
(215) 567-7000
BB/BSA is the only national youth service organization based on the unique concept of a one-to-one relationship between an adult volunteer and an at-risk child to serve as a mentor and a role model. BB/BSA serves as a unified national voice and advocate for the special needs of children, and acts as a central clearinghouse for the exchange of ideas on service delivery and agency administration. BB/BSA serves and represents over 500 affiliated agencies throughout the nation, who can match volunteers with at-risk children.

Boy Scouts of America
1325 Walnut Hill Lane
P.O. Box 152079
Irving, TX 75015-2079
(214) 580-2500
BSA provides an educational program for boys and young adults to build character, train in the responsibilities of participating citizenship and develop personal fitness. The overall program includes opportunities for every age group: Tiger Cubs, Cub Scouting, Boy Scouting, Varsity Scouting, and Exploring. Volunteer adult leaders serve at all levels of Scouting in approximately 380 local councils, 32 areas and 4 regions, and nationally with volunteer executive boards and committees providing guidance.

We are all dependant on one another, every soul of us upon earth.

– GEORGE BERNARD SHAW

Camp Fire Boys and Girls
4601 Madison Avenue
Kansas City, MO 64112
(800) 669-6884
Camp Fire is a national youth agency serving boys and girls from kindergarten through high school. Volunteers and staff help the kids develop self-reliance and self-confidence through a program of informal education and activities.

Christmas In April U.S.A.
1225 Eye Street, NW Suite 601
Washington, D.C. 20005
(202) 326-8268
1-800-473-4229
Christmas in April is dedicated to keeping low income, elderly, and disabled homeowners living in warmth, safety, independence, and dignity through home repair and rehabilitation volunteer services. There are 116 programs that serve 280 communities.

Compeer, Inc.
259 Monroe Avenue, Suite B-1
Rochester, NY 14607
(800) 836-0475
Compeer matches community volunteers with adults and children diagnosed with mental illnesses. These supportive friendships are one-to-one, group or by phone; friends enjoy everything from a conversation to a special community event and schedule their own time together. Call Compeer to volunteer with the program nearest you, to start a program or for more information.

Corporation For National Service
1100 Vermont Avenue, NW
Washington, D.C. 20525
(202) 606-5000
Volunteers in Service to America (VISTA): (202) 606-5212
Retired Senior Volunteer Program (RSVP), Senior Companions and Foster Grandparents: (202) 606-4855
The Corporation functions as a clearinghouse of information and technical expertise for service initiatives nationwide and as a service "venture capitalist," providing funding on a competitive basis for state and national service programs. The Corporation will administer the AmeriCorps program whereby volunteers can serve both part-time and full-time and receive a post-service award of $4,725 to be used for past or present education expenses.
The Corporation will administer Volunteers in Service to America (VISTA), the Retired Senior Volunteer Program (RSVP), Senior Companions and Foster Grandparents. VISTA volunteers work on various projects such as housing, economic development, literacy skills in low-income areas. RSVP offers older adults a meaningful life in retirement

through a wide variety of volunteer service that is responsive to community needs. Senior Companion volunteers provide individualized support and assistance to other adults, primarily the frail elderly. Foster Grandparent volunteers provide one-to-one assistance to exceptional needs children including infants abandoned at birth, addicted to drugs or those who are HIV-positive.

Easter Seal Society For Disabled Children And Adults, Inc.
2800 13th Street, NW
Washington, DC 20009
202-232-2342
The mission of the Easter Seal Society is to provide services that increase independence, function, and productivity of persons with disabilities of all ages, and their families. Volunteer opportunities include special event planning, "day-of" event assistance, office/clerical support, and assistance with Project M.E.D. and Children's Center programs.

Girl Scouts of the U.S.A.
420 Fifth Avenue
New York, NY 10018-2702
(212) 852-8000
Established in 1912, Girl Scouts is dedicated to the development of girls ages 5 through 17 years old or grades kindergarten through 12th. Girl Scouting is a continuous adventure in learning including the importance of community service. 99% of the work is done by volunteers.

Girls, Inc.
30 East 33rd Street
New York, NY 10016
(212) 689-3700
Formerly, Girls Clubs of America, Girls Inc. is a network of nearly 750 program centers. Over 8,000 volunteers are involved in programs to meet the needs of girls (ages 6-18) in their communities. Programs focus on substance abuse prevention, support in math and sciences, and teenage pregnancy prevention. Girls Inc., is also involved in research and development of informal educational programs for girls.

Habitat For Humanity International, Inc.
121 Habitat Street
Americus, GA 31709-3498
(912) 924-6935
1-800-422-4828
Habitat for Humanity is an Ecumenical Christian housing ministry whose objective is to eliminate poverty housing from the world and to make decent shelter a matter of conscience. Through volunteer labor and management expertise and tax-deductible donations of money and materials, Habitat builds and rehabilitates homes with the help of the homeowner. Over 40,000 volunteers have helped build or rehabilitate over 2,000 homes for low-income families in the U.S. and in developing countries.

The Holiday Project
P.O. Box 6347
Lake Worth, FL 33466-6347
(407) 966-5702
The Holiday Project is a nationwide, nonprofit public benefit corporation whose volunteers visit with people confined to hospitals, nursing homes and other institutions during Christmas and Chanukah and on other holidays throughout the year. During the 1991-1992 year, 15,442 volunteers visited with 135,007 people confined in 1,423 facilities in 411 communities in 30 states. Currently, Holiday Project chapters are represented in 36 states.

Laubach Literary Action (LLA)
Box 131
Syracuse, NY 13210
(315) 422-9121
LLA is the U.S. program of Laubach Literacy International. LLA has a network of 1,000 local programs involving more than 100,000 volunteer tutors across the U.S., that reach over 150,000 new readers each year. Programs focus on English as a second language, basic literacy skills, and math and writing skills. Additional services include print and audio-visual resources, consultation, technical assistance and on-site training.

Literacy Volunteers Of America
5795 Widewaters Parkway
Syracuse, NY 13214-1846
(315) 445-8000
LVA combats illiteracy through a network of 455 community volunteer literacy programs in 45 states. These affiliates provide individualized student-centered instruction in basic literacy and English as a second language for adults and teens. They provide pre-service training and technical support to volunteers.

March Of Dimes
1275 Mamaroneck Avenue
White Plains, NY 10605
(914) 428-7100
The mission of the March of Dimes is to improve the health of babies by preventing birth defects and infant mortality through community service, advocacy, and education. There are 112 local chapters. Volunteer opportunities include fund raising, administrative and other support services needed by the local chapters.

Missionaries of Charity
312 29th Street
San Francisco, CA 94131
(415) 647-1889
The Lay Missionaries of Charity make their lives in the world but take the same vows over the same length of time as the sisters. They can be

associated with the apostolate work of the Missionaries of Charity directly, or they can find their own Apostolate to live out their fourth vow to give "wholehearted free service to the poorest of the poor" for their lives. They are religious people but can either be single or married with families.

National Court Appointed Special Advocates Association (CASA)

2722 Eastlake Avenue East, Suite 220
Seattle, WA 98102
(800) 628-3233
CASA (Court Appointed Special Advocates for Children) is a nationwide movement of community volunteers who speak for abused or neglected children in court. The National CASA Association represents 556 CASA programs and 33,000 trained CASA volunteers in all 50 states and Washington, D.C.

National Executive Service Corps (NESC)

257 Park Avenue South
New York, NY 10010
(212) 529-6660
NESC involves senior executive retirees as volunteer counselors for national nonprofit organizations in the areas of education, health, religion, social services and the arts.

National 4-H Council

7100 Connecticut Avenue
Chevy Chase, MD 20815
(301) 961-2800
4-H is part of the cooperative extension service in each county as part of the USDA (Department of Agriculture). 4-H is a co-educational youth education program for ages 5-19. Volunteers can serve as club leaders and/or project leaders.

OASIS

7710 Carondelet Avenue, Suite 125
St. Louis, MO 63105
(314) 862-2933
OASIS (Older Adult Service and Information System) is a national organization operating in 24 U.S. cities. OASIS is dedicated to providing a means for older adults to live independently, to expand their knowledge and to remain productive individuals. OASIS involves over 200,000 volunteers in its programs such as Educational Organizational Services and Intergenerational Tutor Programs.

Special Olympics
1350 New York Avenue, NW
Suite 500
Washington, D.C. 20005
(202) 628-3630
The goal is to provide year round sports training and athletic competition for children and adults with mental retardation to create opportunities to develop physical fitness, courage, build skills, become a part of the community and make friends.

YMCA
101 N. Wacker Dr.
Chicago, IL 60606
(312) 977-0031
The YMCA gives people of all kinds support they need to succeed. The YMCA nurtures the healthy development of children and promotes positive behavior in teens. Local Y's are also reaching out to children and families of low income communities and high risk environments.

YWCA
600 Lexington Ave.
New York, NY 10022
(212) 614-2700
The YWCA is the largest nonprofit community service organization in America, meeting the health and social service needs of 14 million people. It provides value-based prevention programs such as Art Gallery, Art Computer, Language, and Personnel Growth for the healthy development of children and teens and for the strengthening of families. It further offers many athletic facilities.

Volunteers Of America, Inc.
3939 N. Causeway Blvd.
Suite 400
Metairie, LA 70002
(800) 899-0089
VOA is a national nonprofit Christian ministry of service, operating more than 500 volunteer-based programs in over 200 communities in the areas of food, clothing and shelter; health and rehabilitation; corrections; employment; and education.

Youth Service America
1101 15th Street, NW Suite 200
Washington, D.C. 20005
(202) 296-2992 1-800-394-4972
YSA works to promote opportunities for young people to serve their communities and their country. YSA provides assistance to full-time service and conservation corps and school-based service programs. YSA develops, collects, and distributes information and publications on youth service; develops policy on youth service; and assists in the professional development of those who in administer youth service programs.

BIBLIOGRAPHY

VOLUNTEERS AND COMMUNITY
Lawson, Douglas (1991). *Give to Live: How Giving Can Change Your Life*. La Jolla, Calif: ALTI Publishing

Luks, Allan (1992). *The Healing Power of Doing Good*. New York: Ballantine.

Peck, M.D., M. Scott (1987). *The Different Drum: Community Making and Peace*. New York: Simon & Schuster, Inc.

Wilson, Marlene (1990). *The Effective Management Of Volunteers*. Volunteer Management Associates.

FACILITATION AND LEARNING IN GROUPS
Doyle, Michael and David Straus (1993). *How To Make Meetings Work*. New York: Berkeley Books.

Hart, Lois B. (1990). *Training Methods That Work: A Handbook For Trainers*. Menlo Park, CA: Crisp Publications, Inc.

Kaner, Sam (1996). *Facilitator's Guide to Participatory Decision-Making*. San Francisco: Community at Work

Petit, Ann (1994). *Secrets To Enliven Learning: How Develop Extraordinary Self-Directed Training Materials*. San Diego, CA: Pfeiffer & Company.

Spencer, Laura J. (1989.) for The Institute of Cultural Affairs. *Winning Through Participation*. Dubuque, IA: Kendall/Hunt Publishing Co.

Institute of Cultural Affairs (1994). *Technology of Participation: Group Facilitation Methods*. Phoenix, AZ: Institute of Cultural Affairs.

INSPIRATION

Dossey, M.D., Larry, (1993). *Healing Words: The Power Of Prayer And The Practice Of Medicine.* San Francisco: Harper Collins

Easwaran, Eknath (1978). *Gandhi the Man.* Petaluma, CA: Nilgiri Press.

Easwaran, Eknath (1984). *Love Never Faileth: The Inspiration of Saint Francis, Saint Augustine, Saint Paul and Mother Teresa.* Petaluma, CA: Nilgiri Press.

Frangipane, Jr. M.D., Leo (1995). *Touchstones and Wellsprings: The Survivor's Guide.* Mohnton, PA: Hardy Communications.

Johnson, Spencer, (1981). *The Precious Present.* New York: Doubleday & Co.

Nimeth, O.F.M., Albert (1977). *Tenderly I Care.* Chicago: Franciscan Herald Press.

Peck, M.D., M. Scott (1978). *The Road Less Traveled.* New York: Simon & Schuster, Inc.

Peck, M.D., M. Scott (1996). *The Road Less Traveled and Beyond: Spiritual Growth in an Age of Anxiety.* New York: Simon & Schuster, Inc.

Remen, M.D., Rachel Naomi, (1996.) *Kitchen Table Wisdom: Stories That Heal.* New York: Riverhead Books.

Rock, S.J., Leo, (1990). *Making Friends with Yourself: Christian Growth and Self-Acceptance.* New York: Paulist Press

Siegel, M.D., Bernie S.(1986). *Love, Medicine and Miracles.* New York: Harper & Row.

COMMUNICATION
Burley-Allen, Madelyn (1982). *Listening: The Forgotten Skill.* New York: John Wiley & Sons, Inc.

Glasser, William (1984). *Control Theory.* New York: Harper & Row.

Nimeth, O.F.M., Albert, (1977.) *To Listen is to Heal.*Chicago: Franciscan Herald Press.

Tannen, Deborah (1988). *That's Not What I Meant.* New York: Ballantine Books.

Tannen, Deborah (1990). *You Just Don't Understand: Men & Women In Conversation.* New York: William Morrow and Company, Inc.

VIDEOS
Petrie, Jeanette (1986). *Mother Teresa.*Burlingame, Calif: Red Rose Gallerie.

Pomeranz, David and Wernher Krutein (1987). *It's In Every One Of Us.* San Francisco, Calif: New Era Media.

Adventures in Caring Foundation
FACT SHEET

WHO ARE WE?
Adventures in Caring Foundation is a nonprofit, 501(c)3, human service agency, based in Santa Barbara, California. Its mission is to cultivate compassion, and to lift the spirit of those who are sick and lonely.

WHO IS INVOLVED?
A team of one hundred volunteers, ages 16 - 86, who are specially trained in compassionate listening skills, visit patients in hospitals and nursing homes, every week, all year round. A board of directors, committee members, advisors, and auxiliary volunteers also work behind the scenes to move the mission forward.

WHAT DO WE DO?
The Adventures in Caring Foundation teaches and delivers compassion.

1. Adventures in Caring delivers compassion through its all-volunteer Raggedy Ann & Andy Visiting Programs for hospitals and nursing homes. In fifteen years of service, the Raggedy Ann & Andy volunteers have made half-a-million one-to-one visits to patients, and their family members. In addition, Adventures in Caring has begun new pilot programs with student volunteers, who provide psycho-social support to dialysis patients.

2. Adventures in Caring teaches compassion through:

- Compassion in Action, a service-learning program at the University of California, Santa Barbara. This program teaches undergraduate students, who are planning a career in health care, how to communicate with compassion.
- Seminars for volunteer caregivers and health care professionals.
- Workshops and keynote presentations for the general public.
- Publishing learning resources:
  What Can I Say? A Guide to Visiting Friends and Family

Who are Ill. Five thousand copies of this book have been distributed.

Communicating with Compassion: How to Communicate in Ways that Ease the Pain and Lift the Spirit. Two thousand organizations throughout the United States now use this video to educate their staff, students, or volunteers. Proceeds from the sales of these publications help to fund local Adventures in Caring programs.

WHY IS THIS WORK IMPORTANT?

Compassion is fundamental to any healthy, sustainable community. It is the glue that holds people, families, and communities together.

Simple kindness, common decency, healthy relationships, and civic engagement – are all based on compassion. Without compassion selfishness prevails, goodwill decays, suffering crushes the soul, and a community degenerates into a war-zone.

Compassion is often given lip service and taken for granted, but rarely is it deliberately cultivated.

WHY DO WE SERVE?

Adventures in Caring serves all people, and all families, regardless of their illness or injury, age, gender, income, race, or religion.

At first glance, most people think that the Raggedy Ann & Andy program is just for children – yet it has proven effective with patients of all ages, in acute care, subacute, rehabilitation and convalescent hospitals. Raggedys give support not only to the patients, but also to the families and health care staff who care for them.

At present Raggedys visit thirty-five hospitals and nursing homes every week, primarily in Santa Barbara and Ventura counties. However, Raggedys also visit the sick in nine other states.

WHY DO WE DO IT?

There is no pill for loneliness. In the darkest hours of illness or injury, the medicine that lifts the spirit, is compassion. As Mother Teresa of Calcutta said, *"The greatest pain on Earth*

is not the pain of hunger or poverty, but rather the pain of isolation, abandonment and feeling unloved." The solution is human contact, with someone who cares and who listens.

As many as eighty percent of patients in nursing homes have no visitors at all. In hospitals up to thirty percent of the patients can be from out of town, and for numerous other reasons, families or friends are often unable to visit. A serious illness forces us to come to terms with issues that we would rather not think about. Patients in hospitals and nursing homes often have no one to talk to about such issues; no one to listen to their hopes and fears.

The Adventures in Caring Visiting Programs meet this need with a good listener and a friendly face at the patient's bedside.

HOW WE DO IT?

All Adventures in Caring volunteers learn how to communicate with people who are seriously ill. They skillfully deliver four life-affirming things that patients, and their families, need:
• attention • acknowledgment • affection • acceptance.

 Raggedy Ann and Raggedy Andy are non-threatening, well-loved, and easily recognized. They are safe: they don't hurt or deliver bad news. And they don't give advice.

The Raggedys work closely with nursing staff, who choose which patients they should visit. These visits bring comfort, encouragement, and joy to thousands of patients who might otherwise have no visitors.

RECOGNITION

The work of Adventures in Caring has been recognized by:

➤ President Bush, Point of Light Award #407, in March 1991, for outstanding community service.
➤ Rotary International Paul Harris Award.
➤ Los Angeles Times, Family Circle, Parade Magazine, Guideposts Magazine.
➤ CNN News, KCAL News (Los Angeles,) Columbia Pictures with Willard Scott, Hour Magazine with Gary Collins.

HOW DID ADVENTURES IN CARING BEGIN?

Adventures in Caring Foundation was founded in 1985, by Karen Fox. Karen began by volunteering on her lunch hours. Every day, dressed as Raggedy Ann, she brought encouragement to patients at Santa Barbara Cottage Hospital.

Karen spent fifteen years in medical administration, and is a recovered cancer patient. With a special understanding of patient needs "from both sides of the hospital bedrails," Karen recognized that in addition to the physical challenge of battling an illness, patients have a tremendous need for emotional support.

HOW IS ADVENTURES IN CARING FUNDED?

Adventures in Caring programs are supported entirely by private donations and private grants, plus sales of its publications (with no funding from government). Eighty-six percent of funds raised go directly into program.

With your participation and support we can help to alleviate the suffering of those who are sick and lonely; and teach young people entering the health professions how to communicate with compassion. We can plant the seeds of compassion that will produce a healthier community for our children's children.